CW00765508

Classroom Strategies for Children with ADHD, Autism & Sensory Processing Disorders

KAREN HYCHE, OTD, OTR
VICKIE MAETRZ, OTD, OTR

PESI
Publishing
& Media
www.pesipublishing.com

Published by
PESI Publishing & Media
PESI, Inc
3839 White Ave
Eau Claire, WI 54703

Editing: Bookmasters
Layout: Bookmasters
Cover Design: Amy Rubenzer

Printed in the United States of America

ISBN: 978-1-936128-80-8

PESI
Publishing
& Media
www.pesipublishing.com

Table of Contents

Acknowledgments

It is difficult to find just the right words to express our gratitude for the opportunity to write this book. 1 Peter 4:10 tells us "[a]s each has received a gift, use it to serve one another, as good stewards of God's varied grace." God provided us with a gift of knowledge and ability to work with children with special needs. We pray that sharing this knowledge with others will help teachers and students receive the support they need to reach their full potential.

From Karen: Special thanks to my husband, Scotty, for his support and understanding and my family, Becky, Jason, Kolden, Jameson, Jasee Scott, and Jenny and Jim. I am grateful to my parents whose support and love allowed me to accomplish my goals. Special thanks to Vickie for her vision, expertise, and friendship. For all my friends and family, especially Amy, thanks. Much appreciation to my coworkers and friends at the Arc of Walker County for their kindness, support, and tolerance of my often-unorganized schedule. And for the wonderful families that have allowed me to be a part of their lives, thank you.

From Vickie: Special thanks to my family, Travis, John, Tori, and Tyrel, your support and encouragement to follow through has meant a great deal to me. I want to thank all of the parents who have allowed me to be a part of helping growing with their children. God has blessed me with many things and having a friend like Karen to begin this adventure with has been worth all the work.

We want to thank Cody Machala for stepping in and not questioning us when we asked him to do the illustrations for the book.

About the Authors

Karen Hyche, OTD, OTR, has specialized in pediatrics for more than16 years. She received Associate of Science Degree and completed the occupational therapy assistant program at the University of Alabama at Birmingham. She completed her bachelor's degree in health care management at Birmingham Southern College followed by a master's in occupational therapy at Belmont University. She completed her Doctorate of Occupational Therapy at Belmont University in 2003. Karen is Sensory Integration Praxis Test (SIPT) certified through Western Psychological Services and the University Southern California and is an Integration Listening System (ILS) provider.

Karen currently works for The Arc of Walker County in rural Alabama. Her clinical experience includes early intervention, pediatric outpatient services, inpatient psychiatric services, and public school systems. She serves as a fieldwork instructor for the local occupational therapy assistant program. She is also a member of the Alabama Early Intervention ICC and currently serves as the financial subcommittee chair.

Karen lives in rural Alabama with her husband, Scotty. She has two stepdaughters and three grandchildren. She enjoys spending her leisure time gardening, fishing, and camping with her family and is active in the Celebrate Recovery program at her church.

Vickie Maertz, OTD, OTR, has specialized in pediatrics for more than 15 years. She graduated from Belmont University in 2003 with a master's, followed by a doctorate, in occupational therapy. Prior to becoming an occupational therapist she was a certified occupational therapy assistant. Vickie is Sensory Integration Praxis Testing (SIPT) certified through Western Psychological Services and the University Southern California, and is a Berard AIT provider. Her clinical experience includes early intervention, pediatric outpatient services, pediatric home health, and public/private school systems.

She currently owns two private pediatric occupational therapy clinics in Texas. She lectures on the professional level with day care for continuing education training and at a Certified Occupational Therapy Assistant (OTA) program in the Houston area. She currently serves on the board for Court Appointed Special Advocates (CASA) for Kids.

Vickie lives in rural Texas with her husband, Travis, and their grown children. She spends her extra time volunteering for CASA for kids and her churches daycare board.

ILLUSTRATOR

Cody Machala currently attends college while working. He enjoys reading, especially the Bible, hanging out with his friends, the beach and being with his family. Cody's family has encourage Cody and his twin brother to do what their heart's compassion was and to not to let others deter them from their dreams. Cody has a passion for illustrating by using photos that he takes, with ambitions to be a book illustrator. He currently lives in rural Texas with his brother, Gary. His goal in life is to be the person that God planned for him to be.

The main reason why I chose Gary Machala to be the main model for this book is due to his special condition, person, and history. Being diagnosed with Asperser's syndrome, and as a patient of Vickie Maertz, I figured that his presence alone would provide a more deeper, visual understanding of how hard life can be for autistic patients and the wonderful victories that come along with it. Aside from being my identical twin, living with Gary is truly a miracle only God can provide and I'm blessed everyday having him as a big part of my family and part of this book. -Cody

Introduction

With many years of experience, we have answered the same questions over and over. What do I do when . . ." A vast number of wonderful resources are available for each of the diagnosis address in this book. There are websites with incredible information to help as well. Yet teachers still have questions. This book was developed so that teachers could open up a single book and find information as well as solutions about autism, ADHD, and sensory processing disorder. This book was written for teachers so that they have the knowledge to provide modifications and adaptations students need to reach their maximum potential.

Our Senses

We would never learn to be brave and patient,
if there were only joy in the world.
                                        —Helen Keller

1

Our Senses

To understand sensory processing disorder, you must first understand your senses and how they are processed. Most people know their five senses: taste (gustatory), sight (visual), sound (auditory), touch (tactile), and smell (olfactory). There are, however, three more systems. They are the vestibular, the proprioception, and the interception. Each system has an important role in our daily life.

Our olfactory and gustatory systems allow us to smell and taste. Our visual and auditory systems allow us to see and hear. Our vestibular system allows us to stand upright, maintain balance, and move through space. Vestibular receptors are located in our ears. Any head movement activates our vestibular system.

The tactile, or touch, system consists of two types. First, there is light touch. Light touch is produced with little force on the surface of the skin. An example of light touch is a feather brushing across your arm. The second type of touch is deep touch. This sensation takes place with a touch with enough force to be felt in the deep layers of the skin. An example of deep touch is a tight hug for a child or a deep pressure massage for an adult. Our tactile sense also plays a role in safety and security. We bond with infants by holding and find safety in a hug. Touch is an innate human need.

The receptors for the proprioceptive system are located in the muscles and the joints. This system tells us where our body parts are and what they are doing. Input from the proprioceptive system helps us move and manipulate objects without having to look at each body part while it moves, such as when you reach into your pocket to find a quarter rather than a nickel or when, not looking, you reach into your desk to get a pencil rather than an ink pen.

Interception is the system responsible for detecting internal regulation responses, such as respiration, hunger, heart rate, and the need for digestive elimination. When you feel thirsty or feel the need to use the bathroom without someone else telling you to go, your interception sense is at work.

Definitions of Our Senses

- **Visual**—Receptors are located in the eyes
  - Allows us to see
  - Connect with the vestibular system
- **Tactile**—Receptors are located in the skin
  - Two types
    - Deep
    - Light
- **Gustatory**—Receptors are located in the mouth
  - Allows us to taste
- **Olfactory**—Receptors are located in the nose
  - Allows us to smell
- **Auditory**—Receptors are located in the ear and the cochlear nerve
  - Allows us to hear
- **Vestibular**—Receptors are located in the inner ear
  - Allows us to stand upright, maintain balance, and move through space
  - Dysfunctions in the vestibular system can cause anxiety or panic attacks, a need for self-stimulation, abnormalities in muscle tone, and drooling.
- **Proprioception**—Receptors are located in the muscles and the joints
  - Allows us to know where our body parts are and what they are doing
  - Input from this system helps us move and manipulate objects without having to look at each body part while it moves.
  - Gives us information about our position and movement
    - Body awareness
    - Motor skills
    - Social-emotional skills
- **Interception**—Receptors are
  - Responsible for detecting internal regulation responses, such as respiration, hunger, heart rate, and the need for digestive elimination

Sensory Processing Disorder

*Once children learn how to learn, nothing is going to narrow
their mind. The essence of teaching is to make learning
contagious, to have one idea spark another.*
—Marva Collins

2

Sensory Processing Disorder

Children with sensory processing disorders are often the most misunderstood, misdiagnosed, misguided, and frustrating of the "challenging children" for a teacher to have in a classroom.

Jean Ayres, an occupational therapist and an educational psychologist, is known for her work in the area of sensory integration dysfunction, a term she coined in the 1960s to describe a theory used in occupational therapy. She is credited with beginning research into why some children act they way do.

Sensory Processing Disorder (SPD) is the term used in the *Diagnostic Manual for Infancy and Early Childhood* (Interdisciplinary Council on Developmental and Learning Disorders.) to describe regulatory disorder of sensory processing. Throughout the years, the terms used for sensory processing disorder have changed. You may have a parent who says that his or her child has

Sensory Integration Disorder or Dysfunction

Sensory Integration deficits

Three different types of sensory disorders are noted by the Interdisciplinary Council on Developmental and Learning Disorders in the *Diagnostic Manual for Infancy and Early Childhood as Regulation Disorders of Sensory Processing* (73-99):

Type 1 Sensory Modulation Disorder

Type II Sensory Based Motor Disorder

Type III Sensory Discrimination Disorder

Sensory Modulation

Jean Ayres defined modulation as the "brain's regulation of its own activity."

Over-Responsiveness

The child may
- refuse to participate in certain activities,
- become upset or sick when attempting to participate, and
- may push other children in response to stimuli.

The teacher and/or caregiver view behaviors as
- defiance,
- poor social skills, and
- the child being a bully.

This results in
- poor learning,
- poor self-esteem, and
- fewer friends.

The following are examples for each system of what people who are over-responsiveness may experience:

Auditory
- May be bothered by high pitched sounds and frequencies
- Voices may seem louder
- May be startled by unexpected sounds such as doors slamming

Olfactory
- A fight-or-flight response to sudden odors
- Gagging or vomiting because of strong odors
- Dislikes places that use candles or air fresheners
- Dislikes to be around certain people who wear perfume or cologne

Tactile
- Tags in clothing may seem like needles piercing one's skin
- Perceive a simple touch as being a threat
- Poor hygiene due to disliking the feel of water or a washcloth
- Limited participation in art activities

Visual

- Distress caused by fluorescent lights
- Stress caused by flashing lights
- Sensitivity to colors

Vestibular

- Avoidance of physical activities
- Experiences of carsickness

Proprioception

- Avoidance of steps
- Avoidance of tight hugs
- Distress caused by having to move

Interception

- Fright instigated by a pounding heart
- Intense hunger pains, resulting in eating more
- Frequent use of the restroom

Children who are over-responsive to sensory stimuli often present with anxiety and fear. Unexpected stimuli can result in a flight-or-fright response. To the sensory over-responsive child, a slight bump from another student in the hall is scary and painful and may be viewed as a threat. The child may respond by protecting him or herself. In protecting him or herself, however, the child is seen as being "mean" and is quickly labeled as a bully. Consider a child who is over-responsive to tactile input: He or she may scream when presented with finger paint. The child's fear is real, but others view his or her reaction as the child being defiant.

Under-responsiveness

The child may

- not be responsive to injury,
- take longer to respond to commands, and
- lie around or prop up their head.

The teacher and/or caregiver may

- not recognize that the child is injured,
- view the child as being defiant, and
- view the child as lazy or uninterested.

This results in

- injuries,
- poor learning, and
- the child being left out

The following are specific examples for each system of what a person who has sensory under-responsiveness:

Auditory
- May not respond to noises or to one's name being called
- May speak loudly

Olfactory
- May not respond to very strong smells

Tactile
- Fails to react to tactile experiences, such as injuries (i.e., decreased self-protection)
- May constantly touch objects and people
- May be unaware of messy face and wet clothes

Visual
- May stare into bright light
- May line up toys/objects
- May be overly drawn to spinning or stimulating objects

Vestibular
- Does not seem to notice when they are being moved
- Does not register movement effectively enough to decipher when they are dizzy
- May not notice when they are falling, resulting in decreased protective responses

Proprioception
- Enjoys running and crashing into objects
- Has a tired hand after a few minutes of handwriting and seems to press really hard on his or her pencil
- Pushes other team members excessively hard without intending to or realizing it

Interception
- May rarely feel him or herself breathing or his or her heart beating
- May not feel hungry or thirsty often and, because of not sensing the need to do so, may not perform these everyday tasks as often as others do
- Often a slow potty trainer and may develop enuresis because of not feeling the need to eliminate bowel waste or urine before the body begins to perform the task anyway, may not breathe or sweat because of not feeling the need to when his or her body should, may also be diagnosed with interceptive discrimination dysfunction

Under-responsive children are often not identified until they reach school age. These children are often "easy" babies. However, when school starts, their "laidback" behavior is often seen as a sign of disinterest. Children under-responsive to auditory input may take longer to respond to verbal cues. This can be frustrating for teachers giving directions, who often view this as defiant behavior. For children with tactile under-responsiveness, verbal cues may be necessary to remind them to wipe their mouth because these children may not feel food on their mouth or hand and do not know to wipe off.

Sensory Seeking

The child may
- not be able to sit still,
- hit or push others,
- chew on items or "fiddle" with items,
- turn the television or radio up or talk loud, and
- run instead of walk.

Teachers or caregivers may view the child as
- having attention deficit disorder (ADD) or
- being defiant.

This results in
- poor learning experiences for the child,
- the child having difficulty maintaining, and
- the child disliking school.

The following are specific examples for each system that people who are sensory seeking may exhibit.

Auditory
- Often love loud noises or certain sounds
- Have a hard time coping with silence
- May make noises such as humming or whistling
- Often will choose to listen to loud music and may prefer louder surroundings to quieter environments

Olfactory
- Chronically needs to smell things
- May also make sure that their environments are always filled with fragrances and may go to great lengths to bring as much scent into their homes as possible

Tactile

- Like playing with sand and muck
- May run their hands or fingers across walls, railings, or other objects in their environment
- May constantly touch other people

Visual

- May surround themselves in vivid, flashing, or blinking lights
- May stare at fast-moving objects
- May also stare directly at lights

Vestibular

- Often love to spin and rock and are often roller coaster enthusiasts
- In a constant search for motion, which often leads to a diagnosis, be it accurate or not, of attention deficit hyperactivity disorder (ADHD)

Proprioception

- Bumping and/or crashing into and throwing themselves onto furniture
- May roughhouse or wrestle
- May wear tight clothing

Interception

- May need to keep moving because they may also be seeking a pounding or racing heartbeat
- May frequently take large, deep breaths or have a fast rate of respiration
- May experience hunger and thirst sensations as actually feeling good, causing them to not desire to eat or drink because they may not wanting the feeling to go away
- Can also lead to not eliminating bowel and bladder waste, because they may crave the sensation of needing to do so

Sensory seekers are often the daredevils of the class. They are the movers and shakers and touchers and tappers. These children seem to have plenty of energy but just cannot stop. In order to relate, think about when you are hungry. You want a snack, but you really don't know what you want. You look in the cabinets, the refrigerator, and the freezer. You open the cabinet again and finally choose some crackers. You take a bite and realize that is not what you want. You go back to the freezer and search. Children who are sensory seekers are looking for that sensation they are "hungry" for but cannot get what they need.

Sensory-Based Motor Disorder

Children with sensory-based motor disorder have difficulty navigating the world. Their brains do not do what they tell them to do.

The child may

- appear immature,
- be awkward or clumsy, and
- lie around or prop up their heads.

The teacher and/or caregiver may view the child as

- being defiant,
- being lazy, and
- being silly.

This results in

- poor learning for the child,
- the child having few friends or friends that are much younger,
- and the child feeling defeated.

There are two types of sensory-based motor disorder:

Dyspraxia

Postural Disorders

Praxis

Praxis allows us to carry out daily activities. There are four steps involved in praxis:

- Ideation: having the idea
- Planning: the ability to plan how to complete the task
- Execution: the actual task
- Termination: ending task at appropriate timing

If you tell your students, "Now we are going to cut out the circle," they must first have the idea of what to do. That is to get their scissors. Then they have to think about the task and plan what to do. The students then place their fingers in the scissors, hold the paper with the other hand, and begin cutting. Once they have cut out the circle, they must stop and put their scissors and paper down.

Children who have difficulty with ideation will need cues for helping them get the scissors. Children who have difficulty in planning will need directions for each step. Executing the task may be difficult for some children as well. They may have poor coordination or may become tired. Children with difficulty terminating the activity will want to continue cutting. They will repeat the task over and over and may even become upset when required to stop.

Having difficulty with one or more of these steps is called dyspraxia.

Dyspraxia

Dyspraxia is a condition in which a child has difficulty thinking, planning, and carrying out with certain sensory or motor tasks. It is almost as though the child doesn't understand the steps involved in a task or she gets "lost" when attempting to carry it out. Dyspraxia may involve one or more of the sensory systems.

Postural Disorder

A sensory-based postural disorder has a negative impact on a person's muscle tone and balance and on his or her ability to operate his or her muscles own body successfully. The following are examples one might see in someone with a sensory-based postural disorder.

Bilateral Integration and Sequencing

- One-sided weakness (not of neurological origin)
- Decreased arm swing when walking and/or running
- Possible head tilt
- Difficulty using both hands in the middle of the body
- Late emergence of a dominant hand
- Appearance of being lost or of being in a daze

Timing

- Human brain measures time continuously
- Requires a variety of human performance mechanisms (e.g., temporal processing; rhythm perception and production; synchronized motor behavior; etc.)
- Timing is essential to human behavior

Children with bilateral integration and sequencing difficulties have difficulty performing daily classroom tasks. They may not be able to hold their paper while writing or cutting. For them, physical education (PE) activities are often difficult, especially playing ball games, jumping rope, and doing jumping jacks.

Timing difficulties result in their inability to drink from a water fountain, to open doors, and even to put on shoes.

SENSORY DISCRIMINATION DISORDER

Sensory discrimination disorder is defined by the Spiral Foundation as problems discerning and assigning meaning to qualities of specific sensory stimuli, poor recognition and interpretation of essential characteristics of sensory stimuli, and poor detection of differences or similarities in qualities of stimuli, for example, temporal/spatial qualities. Sensory discrimination may involve all senses but most commonly affects the tactile, vestibular, or proprioceptive senses and often co-occurs with dyspraxia and poor skill performance (Benson).

The child may
- be clumsy, and
- be rough or even break toys/pencils.

The teacher and/or caregiver may view the child as
- being defiant,
- being a bully, and
- doing things intentionally to make him or her angry.

This results in
- poor learning experiences for the child and
- the child having few friends.

Tactile Discrimination

- Very "touchy-feely," often inappropriately touching objects or people
- Sloppy (clothes are twisted, do not notice food left on their face following a meal)
- High pain tolerance
- Difficulty locating or naming items when their eyes are closed
- Drops items frequently
- Drools past the expected age
- Mouths objects past expected age
- Poor fine motor skills
- Poor speech articulation

Tactile discrimination is linked to somatodyspraxia.

- Somatodyspraxia is characterized by difficulty planning and carrying out new motor acts in the correct sequence (Cermack).
- Children with somatodyspraxia may learn new skills with assistance; however, they are unable to carry over these newly acquired skills to new motor behaviors. For example, a child with somatodyspraxia may learn to cut along a straight line but may not be able to cut out a square.

Proprioceptive Discrimination

- Clumsier than peers of the same age
- Has difficulty using the correct force when picking up objects
- Is rough with peers
- Walks on toes
- Chews shirtsleeve and/or grinds teeth
- Frequently bumps into objects
- May fall down more than peers of the same age

Vestibular-Based Discrimination

- Has poor awareness of body in space
- Does not know if they are falling

Children with sensory discrimination deficits may drop items constantly. It may appear that they are doing this on purpose, but remember, they are not. Some children may have difficulty putting steps of an activity together. You may have watched the student perform an activity the day before, but today they are unable to perform a similar activity. To a teacher, this is frustrating. It is to a child as well.

Our world is constantly bombarding us with sensory input, from sights, sounds, smell, taste, to movement, touch and input to our muscles and joints that can be very confusing to some children who are unable to process what is going on.

System	General Role
Tactile	Allows us to feel both deep touch and light touch
Gustatory	Allows us to taste
Olfactory	Allows us to smell
Visual	Allows us to see
Auditory	Allows us to hear
Vestibular	Allows us to feel movement
Propriocpetion	Allows us to understand where we are in space
Interception	Allows us to feel/understand internal regulation for hunger, thirst, respiration, and bowel and bladder

Please remember that sensory processing disorder is not a free pass for a child to disrupt the classroom. You, as the child's teacher, know the need for discipline; however, you also need to acknowledge that these disruptions, often the result of sensory issues, can be lessened with the right therapies and accommodations.

Wow, that was a lot of information to take in; however, there is so much more to learn. Never be afraid to seek out an occupational therapist to help clarify any of this information or to learn more details.

SUMMARY OF SENSORY INFORMATION

Sensory Systems			
Sensory Modulation			
Sense	Over-Responsive	Under-Responsive	Sensory Seeking
Auditory	• Certain pitches and frequencies may be bothersome • Voices may seem louder • Easily startled	• Does not respond to noises or name being called • May speak loudly	• Difficulty coping with silence • Makes noises • Listens to loud music • Prefers loud surroundings to quieter environments
Olfactory	• Sudden odors can lead to fight or flight response • Strong odors can lead to gagging or vomiting • Refuse to go certain places or be around certain people due to odor	• May not respond to even very strong smells	• Chronically needs to smell things. • Prefers environments that are always filled with fragrances
Tactile	• Tags may seem like needles piecing their skin • A simple touch can be perceived as a threat • Poor hygiene due to dislike to feel of water, wash cloth • Poor participation in activities	• Fails to react to tactile experiences (decreased self-protection) i.e. injuries • May constantly touch objects and people • Unaware of messy face, wet clothes, etc.	• Likes playing with sand and muck • May run hands or fingers across walls, railings, or other objects in the environment • constantly touch other people
Vision	• Florescent lights may be distressing • Flashing lights may be stressful • Sensitivity to colors	• Stares into bright light • Line up toys/objects • Be overly drawn to spinning or stimulating objects	• may surround self with vivid, flashing, or blinking lights • Stares at fast moving objects • May also stare directly at lights.

(Continued)

Sense	Over-Responsive	Under-Responsive	Sensory Seeking
Vestibular	• Sudden change in head position may cause distress • Avoid physical activities • Car sickness • Fear of heights	• Does not seem to notice when they are being moved. • Does not register movement effectively enough to decipher when dizzy. • May not notice when falling, which can result in decreased protective	• Often love to spin and rock, and often is a roller coaster enthusiast. • Constant search of motion often leads to a diagnosis, be it accurate or not, for attention deficit hyperactivity disorder.
Gustatory	• Picky eater; may only eat specific textures or temperatures of foods	• Does not have food preferences • Enjoys spicy or sour foods	• Constantly eating or drinking • Likes chewy and crunchy foods • Overstuffs mouth
Proprioception	• Avoids movement • Appears rigid or tense	• Poor posture • Poor body awareness • Low energy	• Crashes and into things • Loves contact sports or activities
Interception	• May use bathroom frequently • May over eat • Distressed when hot or hungry	• May not be aware of hunger or thirst • May not notice need to go to bathroom	• May over eat or avoid eating • May avoid going to bathroom

Sensory modulation is often difficult to understand because a child can present with different symptoms or even without symptoms depending on the day. Our sensory responses are based on our physical and emotional well-being. A child who may not feel well or who may not have slept well could have a more difficult day whereas the same child, having slept well, may exhibit no or minimal signs of SPD the next day. You must also keep in mind a child may be sensory seeking in one area and sensory avoiding in another area. For example a child may demonstrate the following symptoms.

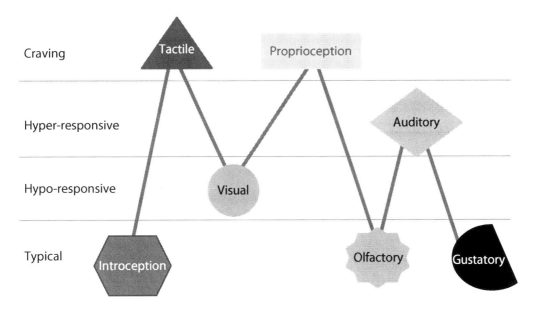

Sensory Discrimination	
Sensory System	**Behavior**
Tactile	• Very "touchy-feely," often inappropriately touching objects or people
	• Sloppy (clothes are twisted, does not notice food left on their face following a meal)
	• High pain tolerance
	• Difficulty locating or naming items with the eyes closed
	• Drops items frequently
	• Drools past expected age
	• Mouths objects past expected age
	• Poor fine motor skills
	• Poor speech articulation
Prioprioception	• Has great difficulty grading movement
	• Rough with peers
	• Walks toe walks
	• Chews on shirtsleeve and/or grinds teeth
	• Frequently bumps into objects
	• May fall down more than peers of the same age
Vestibular	• poor awareness of movement of body in space (gets disoriented easily)
	• knows he's falling, but can't tell which way and can't protect himself

(*Continued*)

Sensory System	Behavior
Dyspraxia	• Difficulty cutting with scissors
	• Difficulty performing various fine motor activities, such as zipping and buttoning clothing without looking
	• Difficulty with dressing and handwriting
	• Have a hard time navigating through crowded hallways or noticing obstacles before collision
	• Unable to use what has been previously learned to help with new tasks
	• Experience anxiety around moving through space or moving up or down stairs
	• May often over or under extend muscles to perform a task, causing one to break things or drop them

Sensory Based Motor	Behavior
Dyspraxia: bilateral integration and sequencing	• One-sided weakness (not of neurological origin)
	• Decreased arm swing when walking/running
	• Possible head tilt
	• Difficulty working at the mid line of the body
	• Difficulty weight shifting
	• Late emergence of a dominant hand
	• May appear lost or in a daze
Postural Based	• Frequently drool and have difficulty keeping things in your mouth
	• Poor posture while sitting or standing
	• Sit in awkward positions, like over the edge of a seat
	• Often lean head forward onto hands, arms, or other objects when working at a desk or eating

Attention Deficit Hyperactivity Disorder

*Each day of our lives we make deposits
in the memory banks of our children.*
—Charles R. Swindoll

3

Attention Deficit Hyperactivity Disorder

Attention deficit hyperactivity disorder (ADHD) is a chronic condition that affects more boys than girls. No single test can diagnose a child as having ADHD. For a diagnosis of ADHD, symptoms must be present before the age of twelve years of age. Although symptoms may be present in very early childhood, the *DSM*-5 notes that symptoms "are difficult to distinguish from highly variable normative behaviors before age 4 years" (American Psychiatric Association 62).

Many diagnoses mimic ADHD. It is very important that all other diagnosis are considered and ruled out. These differential diagnoses include but are not limited to specific learning disabilities, autism, anxiety disorders, and depressive disorders. Students experiencing poor sleep and nutrition can also mimic those with ADHD.

For diagnosis, a licensed health professional must to gather information about the child and his or her behavior in multiple environments. Some pediatricians may assess the child themselves; however, many will refer the family to a mental health specialist with experience in childhood disorders including ADHD. Often the classroom teacher is the first to note the initial signs of ADHD. The behaviors noted in the classroom should be shared with the family. Written documentation is beneficial for both the family and ultimately the physician for a true diagnosis. The physician may send a specific observation form for the teachers to complete. Again this is important for a true diagnosis.

According to the *DSM*-5 there are three subtypes of ADHD:

- Combined type: Inattention and hyperactivity/impulsivity
- Predominately Inattentive without hyperactivity/impulsivity
- Predominately Hyperactivity/Impulsivity without inattention

Symptoms of Inattention

- Easily distracted
- Miss details
- Forget things
- Frequently switch from one activity to another
- Have difficulty focusing on one thing
- Have difficulty focusing attention on organizing and completing a task or learning something new
- Have trouble completing or turning in homework assignments
- Daydream
- Struggle to follow instruction

The child may
- appear "lost,"
- not pay attention, and
- be unable to follow directions.

The teacher and/or caregiver may view the child as
- defiant and
- not smart.

This results in
- poor learning for the child and
- poor grades.

Symptoms of Hyperactivity

- Fidgeting or squirming in his or her seat
- Nonstop talking
- Touching or playing with anything and everything in sight
- Has trouble sitting still
- Constantly in motion
- Has difficulty doing a task quietly

The child may

- appear immature,
- be unable to sit still, and
- talk constantly.

The teacher and/or caregiver may view the child as being

- defiant,
- lazy, and
- silly.

This results in

- the child getting in trouble a lot and
- the child giving up.

Symptoms of Impulsivity

- Impatient
- Blurts out inappropriate comments
- Shows emotions without restraint and without regard to consequences
- Has difficulty waiting for things
- Interrupts conversations

The child may

- appear immature.

The teacher and/or caregiver may view the child as being

- rude and
- silly.

This results in

- poor learning for the child and
- the child having few friends.

Common Medications for ADHD

Stimulants such as methylphenidate and amphetamines are the most common type of medication used for treating ADHD. A few non-stimulant medications are also available. These medications may reduce hyperactivity and impulsivity and may improve children's ability to focus.

Medications affect children differently. Several medications may need be tried before finding one that is successful. It is important for you to know what medication the child is taking and the side effects.

Common side effects include decreased appetite and sleep problems. Less commons side effects include tics or repetitive movements, personality changes, and psychiatric problems, including hearing voices. These symptoms must be taken seriously and be reported to the physician immediately.

Medications do not cure ADHD; they only control symptoms. Children must still learn coping and organizational skills.

Myths about Attention Deficit Disorder	
MYTH	**FACT**
All children with ADD/ADHD are hyperactive.	Some children with ADD/ADHD are hyperactive, but many others with attention problems are not. Children with ADD/ADHD, who are inattentive but not overly active, may appear to be spacey and uninterested.
Children with ADD/ADHD never pay attention.	Children with ADD/ADHD are often able to concentrate on activities they enjoy. But no matter how hard they try, they have trouble maintaining focus when the task at hand appears to be boring or repetitive.
Children with ADD/ADHD choose to be difficult and could behave better if they wanted to.	Children with ADD/ADHD may do their best to be good but still be unable to sit still, stay quiet, or pay attention. They may appear defiant, but that doesn't mean they're acting out on purpose.
Children eventually grow out of ADD/ADHD.	ADD/ADHD often continues into adulthood, so don't expect them to outgrow the problem. Treatment can help a child learn to deal with and minimize the symptoms.
Medication is the only treatment for ADD/ADHD.	Medication is often prescribed for attention deficit disorder, but it might not be the best choice for the child. Effective treatment for ADD/ADHD also includes education, behavior therapy, support at home and school, exercise, and proper nutrition.

Autism Spectrum Disorder

No pessimist ever discovered the secrets of the stars, or sailed to uncharted land, opened a new doorway for the human spirit.
—Helen Keller

4

Autism Spectrum Disorder

According to the Centers for Disease Control (CDC; 2008 Physical Guidelines), autism spectrum disorders (ASDs) are a group of developmental disabilities that can cause significant social, communication, and behavioral challenges.

The *DSM*-5 (American Psychiatric Association) identifies two major diagnosis criteria. The first is persistent deficits in social communication and social interaction across multiple contexts. The second is restricted, repetitive patterns of behavior, interest, or activities. Symptoms must be present in early childhood and result in impairment in social, occupational or other area of function. ASD is defined by severity level. Severity level is defined by the amount of support the individual needs: Level 1 requires support, level 2 requires substantial support, and level 3 requires very substantial support (50).

Many may know of Temple Grandin, PhD; she is well known in different circles for vastly different reasons. In the educational and autistic populations, she is known for overcoming her challenges with autism during a time that not much was known about the disorder; she also has a PhD in animal husbandry and teaches at Colorado State University.

In the book *The Way I See It*, Temple Grandin she explains that individuals with autism have different ways of thinking thus learning. The different types outlined in her book are the following:

> **Visual thinkers**—love art and building blocks. They tend to take longer responding verbally. These children think in realistic pictures, and they tend to produce beautiful drawings.
>
> **Music/Math thinkers**—patterns verses pictures dominate the thinking processes. If you think about it, music and math are made of patterns. These children are good at music and math.
>
> **Verbal thinkers**—love lists and numbers. These children tend to memorize events in history, routes. These children may learn different languages easily. The thinking patterns of these children are different from those of "typical" people; thus, often too much emphasis is placed on what they can't do verses what they can do. (Grandin 19)

Expecting a child with autism to learn the conventional curriculum and teaching methods that have worked for neuro-typical children is to set everyone up for failure. Good teachers understand that for a child to learn the teaching style must match the students learning style.

The following are a few things to remember about a student with autism:

- Learning rules is easy, but learning flexibility in thinking is difficult and must be taught.
- Children on the spectrum have areas of strengths and areas of deficits.
- There are different functioning levels of person's with autism. They are not all the same.

Social communication refers to spontaneous, functional communication and the ability to express a variety of emotions in a meaningful way. Social interaction is the ability of two or more social beings to come into contact communicate or acknowledge one another while being aware of the others and keep them in mind when performing any action. Children with autism often have poor non-verbal communication including limited eye contact. They may have difficulty reading body language and facial expressions. Expressive language may be limited to repeating words or phrases known as Echolalia, difficulty with socially acceptable phrases and expressions may be difficult. For children with average expressive language skills, social interaction may be limited. When approached, children with autism may walk away. They may prefer to play alone.

Restricted, repetitive play behaviors refer to limited interest, specific focus on an object, toy or subject, adherence to specific routines or rituals and repetitive motor movements. Many children with autism fixate on a specific item or may need an item to hold or carry with them at all times. Routines and rituals are often strongly followed. Repetitive motor movements include hand flapping, finger tapping, arm or hand twisting or spinning.

Autism is a spectrum. The DSM-5 identifies the severity as Level 1, 2 or 3. Level 1 is identified as requiring support. Children wit Level 1 autism may need support for basic socialization. They may also need support to assist with schedules and routines. Level 2 is identified as requiring substantial support. Children have marked deficits in verbal and nonverbal communication and social interactions are limited. They have difficulty coping with change and become distressed over change. Restricted, repetitive behaviors are obvious and interfere with function. Level 3 is defined as requiring very substantial support. Children in this category have severe deficits in both verbal and non verbal communication, limited socialial interactions and minimal reactions to social contexts. Behavior is inflexible with extreme difficulty coping with change. Severity level is identified in each criterion. That is a child may be Level 1 in social-communication and Level 2 in restricted and repetitive behaviors.

Autism is a single diagnosis. It may, however, be accomped by other diagnosis. The DSM-5 requires the diagnosis of Autism to specific with or without accompanying intellectual impairment, with or without accompanying language impairment or if it is associated with a known medical or genetic condition or environmental factor. Individuals with autism often have accompanying diagnosis of seizure disorder, anxiety disorders and ADHD.

MYTH	FACT
Autism is a mental health disorder	Autism is a neurological disorder. Studies have revealed abnormalities in brain structure and neurotransmitters in individuals with autism.
Individuals with autism are violent	It is unusual for individuals with autism to act violently out of malice or pose any danger to society. Violent acts usually arise from sensory overload or emotional distress.
Individuals with Autism have savant abilities	
Individuals with autism are cold and lack empathy	Autism often affects an individual's ability to understand unspoken interpersonal communication, so someone with autism might not detect sadness based solely on one's body language or sarcasm in one's tone of voice. But, when emotions are communicated more directly, people with autism are much more likely to feel empathy and compassion for others.
Individuals with autism are unable or unwilling to form meaningful relationships.	Individuals with autism have difficulty with social interactions but can form relationships. They can fall in love, marry and have children.
All indivuals with autism have savant abilities	Only about 10% of individuals exhibit savant abilities. Some have what are considered "splinter skills" meaning they perform above average in one or two areas.
Autism is caused by vaccines	There is no evidence that autism and vaccines are linked in any way, but the idea has undermined parents' confidence in the safety of vaccines. A surge in unvaccinated children, in turn, has led to outbreaks of other childhood diseases that were previously under control.

Other Diagnoses

Your role as a leader is even more important than you might imagine.
You have the power to help people to become winners.
—Ken Blanchard

5

Other Diagnoses

ARE WE SURE?

Other conditions often mimic ADHD, SPD, or ASD. Genetic conditions such as cri-du-chat, fragile X syndrome, and Angelmans syndrome may be mistaken for autism. Tuberous sclerous and Tourette's syndrome may also be diagnosis as ASD. Obsessive compulsive disorder and SPD may be misdiagnosed as ASD. ADHD and SPD are often seen as behavioral issues including oppositional defiant disorder. Environment, nutrition, and sleep can also effect children and result in a misdiagnosis.

Many children, for a variety of reasons, spend much of their time in small dimly lit spaces. They receive constant visual and auditory stimuli from TV, computers, or video games while sitting. Children need to run, play, breathe fresh air, and soak in sunlight. The lack of these things can result in developmental delays and misdiagnosis. Children may find it hard to follow rules at school because the school setting has room to move and run. Student who defy the rules and constantly move around are easily viewed as having ADHD or SPD.

Nutrition is necessary for brain and bone development, focus, attention, and learning. Children are often on the go or may be picky eaters. Some may have limited access to healthy foods. Many children often go for days without a vegetable or a serving of fruit. Children are filled with sugary drinks and snack foods. There are numerous research articles that address diet and ADHD symptoms. According to the Children's Defense Fund, children who do not have access to proper nutrition are much more likely to suffer from psychological disorders, such as anxiety or learning disabilities (July 2010). When a child does not get the required amounts of vitamins, minerals, and other nutrients for health, he or she can be lethargic, lack of energy, and generally fail to thrive. Other research shows that regular habit of eating breakfast as opposed to irregular consumption or skipping breakfast altogether had beneficial influence on attention-concentration, memory, and school achievement (N.S. Gajre et al.)

A failure to thrive academically and socially, resulting from improper nutrition, can have lasting impacts throughout a person's life if it is not corrected early. Poor sleep may also mimic ADHD or SPD in a child. Research shows a significant relationship among ADHD symptoms, sleep disturbance, and diet. Parents who reported more sleep disturbance in their children also reported a higher intake of carbohydrates, fats, and, most particularly, sugar, which was also a significant predictor of nighttime sweating (Blunder et al, 2011). Another research study at Northwestern University Medical Center correlates sleep and daytime behaviors. The study of five hundred preschools found that less than ten hours of sleep increased misbehavior. Children sleeping less than ten hours were consistently at greatest risk for "acting out" behavioral problems, such as aggression and oppositional or noncompliant behavior (Stein, et al). Another study looked at parental reports of nighttime sleep duration for their four-year-old child's typical weekday bed and wake times. Based on these parent reports, shorter nighttime sleep duration in preschool children was associated with higher likelihood of externalizing behavioral symptoms including over activity, anger, aggression, impulsivity, tantrums, and annoying behaviors (Scharf et al.)

Finally, Dr. Michael Breus summarized the results of studies regarding sleep and children:

- Poor sleepers reported being significantly more depressed, without energy, tired, tense, moody, stressed, irritable, and less rested and alert than good sleepers. Interestingly and importantly, they were also more likely to have a negative self-image, which, in light of the preceding information, is not surprising.

- Insufficient sleep has been associated with daytime fatigue, inability to concentrate in school, ADHD, a tendency to doze off in class, problematic behaviors, and lower levels of social skills.

- Persistent sleep problems are associated with learning difficulties throughout the school years. In fact, several studies suggest specific academic deficits, including poor school performance.

- Poorly performing first graders with sleep-disordered breathing showed significant improvement in their grades after treatment.

- Teenage insomnia been related to anger, depression, difficulty with school adjustments, and stress, and studies suggest that insomnia often begins early in life and persists into adulthood.

- Elementary school–age children with disturbed sleep may have poorer coping behaviors and may display more behavioral problems at home and in school.

- Several studies report that more total sleep, earlier bedtimes, and later weekday rise time are associated with better grades in school.

- Those with poor grades are more likely to sleep less, go to bed later, and have more irregular sleep/wake habits.

School and Clinic-Based Services

In spite of the six thousand manuals on child raising in the
bookstores child raising is still a dark continent and no on
really knows anything. You just need a lot of love
and luck.... and, of course, courage.

—Bill Cosby

6

School and Clinic-Based Services

SCHOOL SERVICES VERSUS OUTPATIENT SERVICES

Related Services, in Brief

According to Individual with Disability Educational Act, related services "assist a child with a disability to benefit from special education" (§ 300.24(a)). Related services also help children with exceptionalities to reach their Individual Education Program (IEP) goals and objectives. In fact, in the IEP, the related services section is located directly after the goals and objectives section. The IEP requires the document constructor to list the service to be provided, the location that the service will be provided in, the frequency with which the service will be provided, the projected beginning date of the service, and the anticipated duration of the service. In order to ensure that this section of the IEP is written correctly, it is essential that the service provider of the particular service either attend the IEP meeting or send a written document describing the details of the service that will be provided.

It is important to note that occupational therapy and physical therapy are supplemental services. These services assist children in meeting the educational goals developed by the team. They are not "stand-alone" services.

Related services help children with disabilities benefit from their special education by providing support in needed areas, such as speaking or moving. Related services can include, but are not limited to, any of the following:

- speech-language pathology and audiology services
- interpreting services
- psychological services
- physical and occupational therapy
- recreation, including therapeutic recreation
- early identification and assessment of disabilities in children
- counseling services, including rehabilitation counseling
- orientation and mobility services
- medical services for diagnostic or evaluation purposes
- school health services and school nurse services
- social work services in schools
- parent counseling and training

Common related services are described below.

School-Based Occupational Therapy

According to American Occupational Therapy Association (AOTA), school-based occupational therapy is designed to enhance the student's ability to fully access and to be successful in the learning environment.

This includes working on handwriting or fine motor skills so the child can complete written assignments, helping the child organize himself or herself in the environment (including work space in and around the desk), and working with the teacher to modify the classroom and/or adapt learning materials to facilitate successful participation

School-Based Physical Therapy

According to American Physical Therapy Association (APTA), a school-based physical therapist promotes motor development and the student's participation in everyday routines and activities that are part of the educational program.

The physical therapist performs therapeutic interventions, including compensation, remediation, and prevention strategies and adaptations, with a focus on functional mobility and safe, efficient access, and participation in activities and routines in natural learning environments.

School-Based Speech Therapy

School-based speech and language pathologist services are provided when identified speech-language impairment has a direct impact on a student's educational attainment. Speech-language pathologists work with children in the public school setting who have communication disorders that directly affect their education. Communication disorders include fluency, voice, articulation, language, and hearing impairment.

School-Based Counseling

Counselors are available in the school setting and may have a variety of roles. Counselors facilitate communication among staff, parents, and students. They may provide individual, small group, or classroom counseling to address issues such as anger, social skills, and self-esteem.

It is important to remember that schools generally have two types of counselors: the main counselor who meets with all students in the school setting and one within the special education department who is trained to work with the special education population. Both generally have extensive training in the area of mental health.

The previously discussed services are only available for children with an IEP that demonstrate the need for these services to reach their educational goals. It is not for remediation or rehabilitation.

Many children may not demonstrate the need for related services to meet their educational goals or may not qualify for special education services. Some children will need intense, direct services to address specific areas of concern in addition to school services.

Medical-Based Outpatient Therapy and Counseling

Behavior therapy. Teachers and parents can learn behavior-changing strategies for dealing with difficult situations. These strategies may include token reward systems and timeouts.

Psychotherapy. This allows older children with ADHD to talk about issues that bother them, explore negative behavioral patterns, and learn ways to deal with their symptoms.

Parenting skills training. This can help parents develop ways to understand and guide their child's behavior.

Family therapy. Family therapy can help parents and siblings deal with the stress of everyday life and with the challenges of having a family member with special needs.

Social skills training. This can help children learn appropriate social behaviors.

Support groups. Support groups can offer children and their parents a network of social support and information.

Occupational Therapy and Medical-Based Outpatient Therapy

Occupational therapist evaluate and provide treatment for children with a wide array of deficits for developmental impairments, fine motor skills, activities of daily living, sensory processing, and feeding disorders. Occupational therapists work hand-in-hand with families, physicians, and specialized clinicians. They have training and experience working with the following diagnoses:

- Motor skills disorders
- Autism spectrum disorders (ASD)
- Balance problems
- Visual/perceptual disorders
- Genetic syndromes
- Neurological disorders
- Traumatic brain injuries
- Sensory integration disorders

An occupational therapist may use a variety of treatment approaches including sensory integrative approach. This approach uses fun activities to improve the child's response to sensory stimuli. *Not* all occupational therapist use the sensory integrative approach.

Physical Therapy and Medical-Based Outpatient Therapy

Pediatric physical therapists evaluate and provide treatment for children with motor delays. Physical therapy helps develop the strength and range of motion children need to move through their environment easily and effectively. Physical therapy assists children in meeting their developmental milestones such as sitting, standing, crawling, and walking. They also assess the need for splints and braces. Physical therapists are also trained in the sensory integrative approach.

Speech Therapy and Medical-Based Outpatient Therapy

Speech-language pathologists assess and treat children who experience difficulty with communication. Assessment and treatment of children with developmental speech-language delay or disorder, including children with autism, cerebral palsy, and childhood apraxia of speech (difficulty with the motor skills planning required to produce speech sounds). Treatment also includes cognitive-communication assessment and treatment and evaluation and use of augmentative/alternative communication.

Children may need to see a specialty physician. The following are a few examples.

Pediatric Psychiatrist

A pediatric psychiatrist can also be called a child psychiatrist. All psychiatrists are medical doctors who have completed medical school. They are highly specialized doctors skilled at working with children who exhibit mental disorders or who have developmental conditions such as ADHD, specific learning disabilities, or autism. Psychiatrist address both medication and behavior.

Pediatric Psychologist

Psychologists have a doctoral degree in psychology. Clinical psychologists provide psychological evaluation and treatment for behavioral and emotional problems through counseling. Psychologists address such issues as anxiety and depression, ADHD, and autism.

Pediatric Neurologist

A pediatric neurologist is a medical doctor that has been specially trained to understand a child's developing nervous system, which includes the brain, the spinal cord, muscles, and nerves, and to treat diseases that affect the nervous system. Services include evaluation and treatment of seizure disorder, Tourette's syndrome, autism, and sleep disorders.

SPECIFIC TREATMENT APPROACHES

We feel it is important to educate you on some types of treatment approaches that parents may seek outside services for. Following is a basic overview of some of the treatments.

Applied Behavioral Analysis

Applied behavioral analysis (ABA) is simply the application of behavioral principles, to everyday situations, that will, over time, increase or decrease targeted behaviors. ABA has been used to help individuals acquire many different skills, such as language skills, self-help skills, and play skills; in addition, these principles can help to decrease maladaptive behaviors such as aggression, self-stimulatory behaviors, and self-injury. There is a formal credentialing within the profession of behavior analysts coordinated by the Behavior Analyst Certification Board.

Listening Therapy

Listening therapy (LT) is a therapeutic program using specific sound frequencies and patterns to stimulate the brain. LT is based on the theory of neuroplasticity, which refers to brain changes that occur as a result of experience. Several listening therapies are available including, but not limited to, the Integrated Listening System (ILS), Vital Links, Berard auditory integration training, and The Listening Program.

Neurofeedback

Neurofeedback is biofeedback for the brain. Neurofeedback is an operant conditioning tool that helps retrain the brain. Feedback is commonly provided using a video game. The training is intended improve cognitive function, attention, mood, anxiety, and behavior. It helps quiet the mind.

Interactive Metronome

Interactive Metronome (IM) is a game-like auditory-visual platform that engages the patient and provides constant feedback at the millisecond level to promote synchronized timing in the brain. IM is an evidence-based, engaging therapeutic modality that improves cognitive and motor skills. It assists with attention, coordination, language, processing, and reading and math fluency, it also helps with control of impulsivity and aggression.

By addressing timing in the brain with IM alongside functional therapy interventions you are not only addressing areas of ability that impact achievement and independence but also the heart of the problem, that of deficient neural timing within and between regions of the brain that are underlying many of the problems you are working on in therapy.

Elimination Diet

Many parents are choosing elimination diets such as gluten-free and/or dairy-free diets. So what does this mean? Gluten is found in wheat, rye, and barley and is used as an additive in many foods and products. Children on gluten-free diets must avoid these foods at all times. A dairy-free diet contains no milk, cheese, butter, cream cheese, cottage cheese, sour cream, ice cream, whey, casein, or foods that contain any of these ingredients. Again, these food products must be avoided at all times.

CONVERSATION WITH PARENTS

It is sometimes difficult to have a conversation over what might be a unwelcomed subject to a parent. Listed are some ways to bring up things without offending anybody.

One way to address concerns that affect students such as sleep and nutrition is to provide simple parent education. You may want to consider a monthly "newsletter." The newsletter would go out to all your students, and therefore would not single out a specific child or children. The newsletter would simply provide information that the parent may or may not choose to use. In addition, the newsletter would provide general information such as test dates and upcoming projects. The following is an example.

Some parents, however, may need a more direct approach. If this is necessary, make sure you have plenty of resources available and specific examples of your concerns. Make sure you have the support of other personnel such as the occupational or speech therapist and, of course, administration. The following is an example of how you can document your observations so that you can provide specific information when needed.

Class News Letter

Information

It is often hard to get back into a school routine. Over the summer, many children had the opportunity to stay up late and sleep in. Not sleeping enough or not sleeping well, however, can affect your child's ability to learn. So how much sleep does your child need?

> **3-6 Years Old: 10 - 12 hours per day**
>
> **7-12 Years Old: 10 - 11 hours per day**
>
> **12-18 Years Old: 8 - 9 hours per day**

This Month

Science: We will be learning about the earth. The month will end with the building of a volcano!

Math: Multiplication. We will work on 2x – 5x this month. Study guides will be sent home each Tuesday.

Spelling: Weekly spelling words will

Projects

Each student is required to complete a report for history. The report should be a two page description of our state. It must require the state bird, flower, tree and flag. The report is **due Thursday September 22nd.**

Date	Activity	Childs response	Comments
8/21/13	Finger Painting. All students were given a small bowl of paint and paper and asked to use pointer finger to paint a house	Child said, "I don't want to," when encouraged began to gag	
8/25/13	Standing in line	Pushed a peer. When asked why, he said, "He hit me."	This was observed by another teacher, and the peer simply bumped into him.
8/30/13	Pizza for lunch	Refused to pick it up and began to gag	
8/30/13	Playing outside	Screaming because a rock was in his shoe.	Took more than 5 minutes to calm after rock was removed

Once this information is presented, have information regarding the possible concern, in this case, tactile defensiveness. There are many checklists available online that can be printed and presented to the parents. It is very important to explain how your concerns effect the child's education and daily function. Parents need to know for example why not finger painting is such a big deal. Do not make them feel like this is an attack on their children; you want to make this a team effort for the best interest of the child.

Date	Activity	Childs response	Comments
8/19/13	Math	Fell out of desk	
8/20/13	PE	Refused to participate in scooter bard activity	
8/21/13	Reading	Refused to read aloud	
8/22/13	Reading	Fell asleep	Child said he was playing video game late
8/23/13	PE	Refused to participate in basketball. Said he didn't have to	

Classroom Design

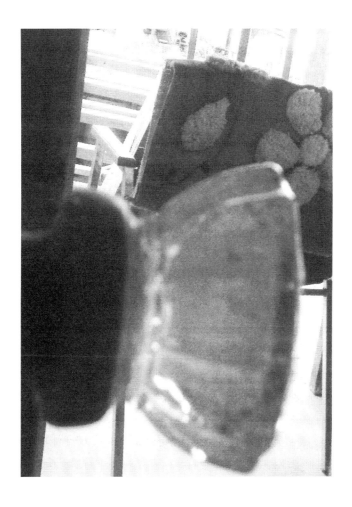

Treat people as if they were what they ought to be, and you help them to become what they are capable of becoming.

—Goethe

7

Classroom Design

CLASSROOM SETUP

There are many things to consider when setting up your classroom. Of course, you want your classroom to be interesting and an environment conducive to learning. However, what is good learning environment for one child may not be for another. You must consider all aspects of your classroom, including:

Lighting	Smells
Walls	Seating
Sounds	Desk arrangement
Organization of room	

Lighting
Possible Problems with Lighting

Florescent lights have a low hum that can be very distracting to children who are overly sensitive to sounds.

Florescent lights blink occasionally and are distracting to children who are over sensitive to visual stimuli.

Sunlight may cause a glare in the classroom
Bright lights including sunlight may cause distress.

Possible solutions

Fluorescent light covers are safety approved and available in a variety of colors. This eliminates glare and provides a calming environment.

Turn off the overhead lights and use battery operated lights.

A "safe area" can be used. This is a designated area that, in this case, is dark and confined. A tent or large cardboard box is a good option. Inside the safe area, provide a battery-operated push light. This will provide enough light for the student to engage in academic activities.

For children who are especially sensitive to lights, consider use of sunglasses, especially outside. Sunglasses with colored lenses are available and will allow you to see the child's eyes.

Closing blinds will decrease lights and outside distractions.

Do not place the visually sensitive child's desk near the window.

Walls

White walls are the most common color for school walls. Some teachers choose to add color such as reds and blue.

Possible Problems with the Color of the Walls and the Wall Decor

White walls may be a little too institutional for all of us. Bright colors on walls, however, may be overwhelming and visually distracting.

Consider posters and pictures on the walls. How many are you putting up? What colors are they? Is it difficult to focus on one specific item posted?

Possible Solutions

If it is necessary and important to place specific materials on the walls consider:

1. Placing specific information in sections of the room
2. Placing one poster in the front of the room while another one on a side wall. This will help children avoid becoming over stimulated or staring at the large amount of visual stimuli.
3. If it is necessary to place multiple items in one location, can those items be covered when not in use? For example, kindergarten classes need the days of the week, letters, numbers, and weather posted in front of the rug for morning circle time. After circle time, a solid colored sheet can be used to cover this information. Simply place Velcro across the top of a sheet and on the wall above the posters; the sheet is easily removed and replaced. For very creative teachers with a budget, posters can be placed on the wall but hidden behind shutters attached to the wall.

Sounds

The noise level inside and outside the classroom as well as the types of sounds may cause distractions for students.

Possible Problems with Sound

Sound cannot be totally avoided. Sounds from other students, outside sounds, sounds from the hallway, lunchroom noise, and echoes in the gym are always present. Some children are hypersensitive to sounds and can hear the conversations in the hallway, which can be very distracting. Student may also be sensitive to the buzzing of lights or air-conditioning units, sounds you may not notice.

Possible Solutions

Noise-reducing headphones

Earplugs, small ones that fit snuggly into the ear. These are easy to find in sporting good sections of stores. Parent permission for earplugs is necessary.

Ear buds or headphones for MP3 player

Smells

Not everyone smells the same smells

Possible Problems with Smells

A child may be hypersensitive to smell and become distracted by your morning coffee or a student's cologne or perfume or bath soap. The trash can close by or even the smells in the cafeteria can be too much for some children.

Cleaning supplies, candles, and fragrant sprays may result in tantrums or gagging for these students.

Possible Solutions with Smells

Be aware of your bath soap or perfume. Keep in mind some children may not like a teacher or other students based on how they smell.

The child's desk should not be near the teachers. Teachers usually place the trash can near their desk. Their snacks and coffee are also on their desk.

Be aware of cleaning supplies used. A child may even refuse to leave the classroom when the floor is being mopped.

Seating

This includes the child's seat and arrangement of desk.

Possible Problems with Seating

Many children have difficulty sitting still or sitting up straight. For children who are tactile defensive, placing desk too close together can be stressful.

Seating Arrangement

Children who are easily distracted and overstimulated should be placed away from windows and doors. In front of the teacher is usually the first option but not always the best choice. The teacher's desk is full of items that the student can focus on or attempt to reach and fidget with. The student may spend time attempting to engage the teacher in conversation as well.

Place desk arm's length apart. This will keep students from leaning over to touch other students. It will also allow students to walk up and down aisles with their books with minimal bumping.

If tables are being used, space students' desks as far as part as possible. Use visual boundaries. Visual boundaries can be drawn in chalk on the table or colored tape (masking tape, painter's tape, or duct tape) can be used. The same strategy can be used to ensure the students chair remains in place.

Visual boundaries can be used on the floor as well. Place tape on the floor, where the student is to sit. Carpet squares are a good alternative as well. If students are required to sit on a rug, specify where on the rug the student should sit as "the yellow circle."

The Chair

Believe it or not, the chair itself may be too hard for a student to sit on. As a teacher, your seat it cushioned and the child gets the hard plastic chair.

Take a look at the height of the chair: Are the child's feet touching the floor or dangling in the air? It is difficult to maintain balance in a chair when your feet do not touch.

How long are students required to sit?

Possible Solutions and Alternatives

Sitting in hard chairs for hours is not easy especially for students with the diagnosis mentioned thus far. Children seeking vestibular and proprioceptive input just need to move. Despite your attempts to have the child sit, he or she just can't. The use of a ball as a chair, sensory chair cushion, or chair wedges provide proprioceptive and vestibular input while seated at his or her desk.

1. Cushions

   a. A regular chair cushion may provide some benefits. It will need to be a thick cushion that still allows the students feet to touch the floor

   b. A therapy disc cushion is a plastic disc filled with air. One side is smooth, and the other is bumpy. The disc allows the student slight movement in his or her chair. It is important that the student's feet are still flat on the floor. If the student's feet do not touch the floor, place a book on floor to prop his or her feet on.

   c. A desk wedge is similar to a disc cushion only it is shaped as a wedge.

2. Balls

   A yoga ball or a therapy ball can be used. Again the student's feet must be able to touch the floor.

   Consider

   Balance—a student must have good balance.

   Strength—trunk strength is required for a student to maintain upright position.

   Endurance—The student must be able to maintain his or her balance for an extended period.

The use of balls as chairs may seem like a bad idea in a classroom. For children who truly need this type of sensory input, it can improve their attention and allow you to focus on the entire class. One research study showed the use of a ball chair appeared to have a positive effect on in-seat behavior for the child who had the most extreme vestibular-proprioceptive-seeking behaviors. However, children with poor postural stability were less engaged when sitting on the therapy ball chair (Bagatell, et al). Remember, even children who are proprioceptive and vestibular seeking will not need or benefit from a ball chair, a cushion, or a wedge all the time.

Another concern with the use of ball chair is that other students will want to use it. Allow each student to have a turn sitting on the ball chair. Most will not like it or will only like it for a short time. If at all possible, purchase one more than you need. That will allow other students to have the opportunity to use the ball the chair if they choose.

Finally, rules must be established. You can have the students help you make the rules. This often helps ensure rules to be followed. Of course, you will guide their rule making.

Rules for ball chairs

You must ask before getting the ball chair

The ball only leaves the floor when carried to and from your desk.

You may bounce gently on the ball.

Your bottom must remain on the ball.

Your feet must remain on the floor

You may not poke the ball with a pencil, pen or other object

You must not remove the plug.

Children who are proprioceptive and vestibular seeking may also have sensory motor dysfunction. Although they need the movement a ball chair provides, they are unable to maintain their balance on the ball. For these students you may consider a ball chair, which provides a frame for the ball that provides stability and support.

The goal for all students is to complete their work so they can learn. Sitting for hours may actually hinder the student's ability to achieve this goal, and there are other alternative to sitting in a chair. This may too seem like a bad idea, but establishing rules and boundaries will eliminate chaos. It will also help ease the battle of "sit down" and allow you to focus on the entire class.

Alternatives to Desks

Standing: Designate a standing work area. You can do this by using a throw rug or tape on the floor so students have a visual boundary. Then simply tape the worksheet to the wall. A clipboard fastened securely to the wall will work as well. To ensure all students have equal opportunity have more than one standing area available.

Lying on the floor: This area is best for the back corner of the room. A wedge or pillows can be used for the student to prop on. A clipboard makes a nice writing surface.

Beanbag: This is a relaxing alternative especially for reading. For children with low endurance and muscle tone, sitting upright in a chair all day can be exhausting. A beanbag provides the opportunity to rest can allow the child to refocus.

Desk Arrangement

Many times we place the students we "need to keep an eye on" in front of the teachers desk. For students who are tactile seeking or impulsive this is tempting. The teacher typically has items on her desk such as pictures, pens, pencils, and papers that a student would love to "fiddle" with. For children who are sensitive to smell or who are seeking oral input, this is not a great place to sit either. The garbage can is usually next to the teacher's desk. The smell of multiple items may result in the student gagging or becoming upset. A student may also attempt to place items from the trash can in his or her mouth. Students are usually required to walk to the teachers' desk to turn in papers or throw items away. For children who are easily distracted or impulsive this is an opportunity to talk to peers. For children who are tactile defensive, this can cause anxiety and fear. The thought of a peer bumping into him or her, the possibly of being hit by a backpack, or even a pat on the back from the teacher is frightening.

Students who are visually over sensitive or inattentive should not be seated near a window. Students who present with self-stimulating behaviors or who may need movement breaks are best seated at back of the class. This will allow them the opportunity to move around without disrupting the class.

You need space for

Standing	Walking
Lying down	Quiet area/calm down
Dim lights	Daily school supplies
Homework	Schedules

Organization of classroom

Having a place for everything reduces stress for both you and your students. Label areas and be consistent in where items are placed. Do not assume your organization is obvious. Be sure and explain to the students how the room is organized.

Do you have a daily schedule posted?

Do you write down daily assignments and homework for the students?

Where do students place homework assignments?

Where are supplies kept?

Do you have books or worksheets for students when they finish an assignment before other students? If so, be sure students know where the work is located.

If the student has task or different work items is there a space for them to find and return their work?

EXAMPLES OF CLASSROOM SETUPS

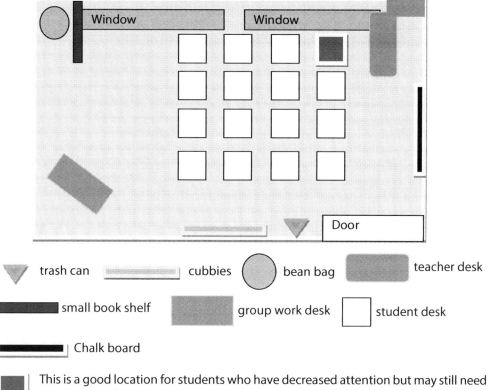

▽ trash can	▭ cubbies	◯ bean bag	teacher desk
▬ small book shelf		group work desk	▢ student desk
▬ Chalk board			

This is a good location for students who have decreased attention but may still need to utilize a "safe place" as long as blinds or shades are used.

Minimal disturbance to other students leaving desk and going to "safe place."

The "safe place" utilizes a bookshelf to provide a visual block.

The trash can has been moved to avoid odors.

The teacher has a table to the side of desk. This allows personal items to be placed near the teacher but away from students. This is especially important for a child that is tactile seeking.

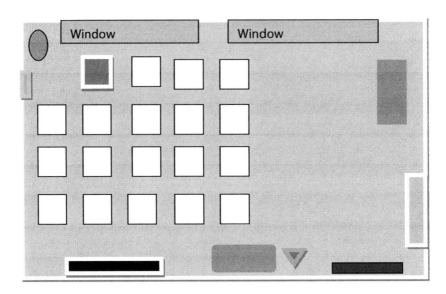

Student desk are facing chalk board

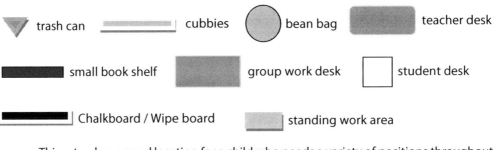

trash can	cubbies	bean bag	teacher desk
small book shelf	group work desk		student desk
Chalkboard / Wipe board	standing work area		

This setup has a good location for a child who needs a variety of positions throughout day. This provides a space for child to stand and complete work or even an area to sit on floor without disrupting other students.

RESOURCE ROOM SETUPS

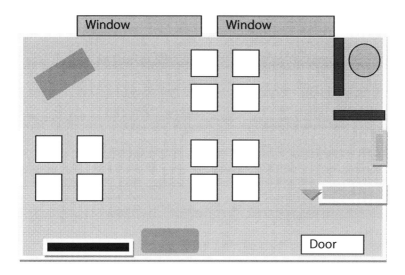

Students desk are facing blackboard

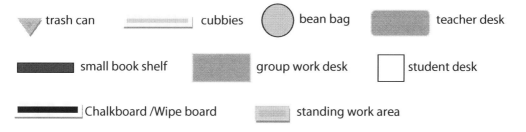

trash can   cubbies   bean bag   teacher desk

small book shelf   group work desk   student desk

Chalkboard /Wipe board   standing work area

This room allows space between desks.
There is a "safe space" is in the corner
A standing work area is provided as well.

Sensory Strategies

I think a hero is an ordinary individual who finds strength to persevere and endure in spite of overwhelming obstacles.

—Christopher Reeve

8

Sensory Strategies

There are many different types of sensory strategies, of which a few are explained in the following. As always, if you have any additional questions or strategies that you would like to implement, feel free to contact your school's occupational therapist.

Schedules

    General written

    General picture

    Specific written

    Specific picture

Teaching Methods

    Learning pyramid

    Video modeling

    Personal stories

    Daily report card

Strategies for Learning

    Weighted vest/weighted lap blanket

    Movement breaks

    Fidgets

    Oral motor activities and tools

    Positioning (sit, stand, lay)

    Headphones/music

SCHEDULES

Daily schedules assist with the fear of change and uncertainty. Schedules also provide students with reminders decreasing the teachers need to remind, reassure, or redirect. For many students, a daily schedule can reduce behaviors dramatically.

Types of schedules

General written

General picture

Specific written

Specific picture

General written schedule may look like the following example and can be placed on the wall. If schedule changes write it on wipe board or chalkboard. Explain to students that the schedule will always be in this location.

8:00-8:30	Reading
8:30-8:50	Vocabulary
8:50–9:30	Math
9:30–9:45	Morning Break

General picture schedule

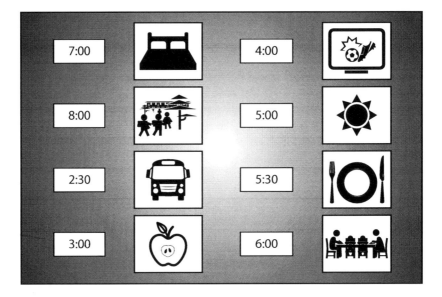

Specific schedules may be more detailed in time or task. The following is an example of a task-specific schedule that provides both written and picture cues.

End of the Day

1. Get Notebook

2. Get Lunchbox

3. Put In Bookpack

4. Go Home

How to Make and Use Picture and Written Schedules

A variety of items can be used to make the schedules. For example, a paint stick provides a nice vertical surface and can be placed anywhere. A bulletin board is perfect for a classroom schedule. Folders provide a way to cover individual schedules for privacy. For older children, a binder provides both privacy and function.

If the child needs a picture schedule, there are many choices. Programs that provide both pictures and templates are available for a fee. One such program is Boardmaker by Mayor Johnson, which is available at http://www.mayer-johnson.com/boardmaker-software-family.

Clip art or photographs of items and the task may also be used.

For children who are able to use written directions, you may write or type them. Be sure to use a font easily read by the child. Use short, simple sentences. Bullet or number each task.

A combination of written and pictures are great for use for the entire classroom.

Printing, laminating and velcroing picutres to implement picture schedules can be timely and costly. A nice alternative are magnetic picture symbols which are available at schKIDules.com

Picture schedule apps are also available for both iTunes and Android. For children using tablets this allows easy access to their daily schedule.

Schedule use must be taught. Do not assume just because you wrote a schedule on the board the class understands why it is there. Explain to the class or the student why they have a schedule. Also explain where the schedule will be located. It needs to be in the same place all the time. Make sure they understand the schedule. If you have chosen to use pictures make sure they know what each picture refers too.

TEACHING METHODS

Every student learns differently. We know there are auditory learners, visual and kinesthetic learners. Retention rates vary depending on teaching styles. The learning pyramid shown indicates the average student retention rate according to teaching styles.

Learning Pyramid

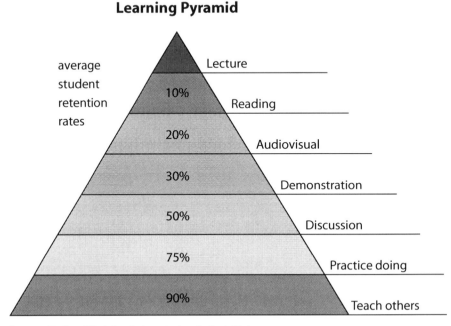

Source: National Training Laboratories, Bethel, Maine

The preceding illustration is a reflection of "typical" students. Do you think children with poor attention retain 10% of what they read? What about those who are visually overstimulated? Think of ways you can incorporate practice and allowing students to teach. You are most likely already incorporating these methods. So just focus on these methods a little more.

Video Modeling

Video modeling is a teaching technique that involves having a student watch a model perform a target skill on a video and then practice the skill that he or she observed.

Video modeling can be used to teach a wide variety of skills: communication skills, daily living skills, social skills, and academic skills

Evidence

Video modeling meets evidence-based practice (EBP) criteria with having completed eight single-subject studies. The evidence-based research suggests that video modeling can be effectively implemented with learners from early childhood through middle school. This practice may prove useful with high school age learners as well, though no studies were identified to support its use at this age level (Framzone and Collet-Klingenberg).

The first step of video modeling is to choose the targeted area. An area of concern may be disrupting the class, walking down the hall, or going through the lunch line.

Data regarding the behavior should be gathered. For example, a student may interrupt conversations during class and average of three times per day over a two-week period.

The next step is to choose what type of video model to use. There are four different types of video models:

Basic video modeling: Using a child or adult "actor" to demonstrate the target skill or act out an exchange. The actor can be familiar or unfamiliar.

Video self-modeling: This video is produced with the child as an active member of the video. You must capture carefully planned or even an edited video which shows the person (child) engaging in appropriate positive behaviors, completing a task, responding to verbal commands or prompts (you need to edit the cues from final video), or handling a difficult situation in a more adaptive manner.

Point-of-view modeling: This video is viewed from the perspective of what the student would see, hear, and say in the targeted situations. This type of video will require additional time and editing.

Video prompting: Video prompting demonstrates each step of a task. One step is shown, and once the student masters that step, then the next step is shown.

If you are using students in the video, parent permission must be obtained. There are video models available for purchase.

Once the type of video has been determined, write a "script" and then shoot the video. The video should be simple and concise. A two- to three-minute video is best.

The video should be shown to the student daily. If the video is targeting a specific time of day, show it prior to that task. If it is a general area of concern, such as disrupting the class, designate a time for the child to watch the video.

Keep data during this time. As the targeted behavior decreases, you will decrease the amount of time the child watches the video. You may decrease it to three times weekly, once a week, and then once a month. Once the task is mastered or the behavior has stopped, the video is no longer shown.

Personal Stories

Personal stories are targeted to a specific child for a specific event. Personal stories can be in a book format or e-format. Write the book in language appropriate for the child. It does not need to be long. You want to keep the child's attention so he or she will understand the content. Use pictures. Because it is a personal book, if possible, use the child's picture.

An example of a personal story would be going on a field trip during which there are many steps that we do not think about and from which the increase in excitement, visual, and auditory stimuli that is happening at the same time can become overwhelming to a child. A personal story about what to expect on the field trip can be read daily, prior to the trip to ease anxiety and set expectations.

A small photo album may be used to make the book. You can print out pages of the book, punch holes in the side, and use ribbon to tie the pages together. Or you may make a digital book using PowerPoint format.

Museum Day

On the day the class goes to the museum, I will follow my friends to the bus.

Page 1

I will sit in my seat on the bus the entire way to the museum.

Page 2

When the bus is parked, I will follow my friends inside.

Page 3

I will be able to look at all the pretty things but I cannot touch.

Page 4

I must walk with my friends and teacher so I can stay safe.

Page 5

I will get to eat lunch with my class at the park before we go back to school.

Page 6

I will sit down in my seat on the bus for the long ride back to school.

Page 7

Daily Report Cards

Daily report cards allow teachers and parents to address areas that interfere with a child's academic success and measure important improvements. Daily report cards work by monitoring and recording specific areas each day at designated times of the day. The child is required to bring the DRC home and have a parent sign. The book *Daily Behavior Report Cards: An Evidence-Based System of Assessment and Intervention* (Volpe et al.) describes in detail the development and use of daily report cards. The following is a brief overview:

How to develop a daily report card:

- Set Goals
  - 3 to 8 clearly defined goals
  - Can be academic, conduct, and peer relations
  - Define goal
- Make it attainable
  - No one does anything 100% of the time
- Explain to student
  - Explain purpose
  - Explain Procedure

- Develop a home reward system if applicable. The reward should be simple and reasonable.
- Review at a regularly scheduled time such as once a week or at the end of each day.
- Monitor and modify

The following is an example of a daily report card:

	Morning	Afternoon
Completes classroom assignments, by himself, 1 out of 4 times	yes/no	yes/no
Raises hand to ask question or make statement 2 out of 5 times	yes/no	yes/no
Stays in line, in place, 3 out of 5 times	yes/no	yes/no
Complies with teacher request 2 out of 4 times	yes/no	yes/no

On the third week, review of the daily report card shows significant improvement in all areas. Goal 3 is no longer needed. The teacher and the student discuss progress and the student helps the teacher set new goals.

	Morning	Afternoon
Completes classroom assignments, by himself, 4 out of 5 times	yes/no	yes/no
Raises hand to ask question of make statement 4 out of 5 times	yes/no	yes/no
Complies with teacher request 4 out of 5 times	yes/no	yes/no
Follows PE rules 3 out of 5 times	yes/no	yes/no

Weighted Vest and Weighted Lap Blanket

Deep-pressure, weighted vests, and blankets can be highly beneficial to some children with autism, sensory integration disorder, ADHD, and other neurological disorders. Based on the sensory integration framework, the added weight or pressure provides the child with unconscious information from their muscles and joints. Thus, they are able to integrate sensory information, calm, become more organized, and improve their ability to concentrate and learn.

There are no standard guidelines for how much the vest should weigh; however, common practice is to use five percent of the child's body weight as a starting point. Therapists and teachers should observe and report any outcomes or changes in the child's behavior when wearing the vest and make adjustments based on the child's response. The vest should be worn for a minimal of 20 minutes to a maximum of two hours. Weighted vest are only recommended after speaking to an occupational or physical therapist first.

Weighted lap blankets may be used as well. This is simply a small weighted pad that is placed in the child's lap. Use *only* under the supervision of an occupational therapist who can assist in the proper weight. Too much weight can result in overstimulation and/or injury.

Heavy Work Activities

These are activities that provide the student with proprioceptive input. Activities that require the student to use large muscles can be both calming and alerting. Heavy work activities can be incorporated into the students' routine to maintain focus and attention. Activities may also be encouraged as needed.

> Placing the chairs on tables
>
> Passing out books
>
> Cleaning the chalkboard
>
> Sweeping the floor

> PE is a great time to incorporate heavy work.

> Propelling self on the scooter board
>
> Rope ladder
>
> Running laps
>
> Running up/down blenchers
>
> Jumping rope
>
> Push-ups
>
> Jumping jacks

> The following activities can be done throughout the day:

> Palm presses
>
> Wall push-ups
>
> Marching while seated or in place

Movement Breaks

Research shows that 15 minutes of exercise in the classroom improved performance on cognitive tests conducted later in the day (Kerby). This study used yoga poses involving gross motor movements. The results of the study

- demonstrated that incorporating motor breaks into the afternoon routine significantly decreased the students' off-task behaviors.
- demonstrated how the students' perceptions of their abilities to focus and remain on-task in the afternoons increased due to the motor breaks.
- showed that the implementation of motor breaks was successful in decreasing students' off-task behaviors and increasing their perceptions of their abilities to focus and remain on task.

> Taking a movement break is great to get everyone refocused.

Before implementing movement breaks into your classroom schedule, give a general explanation to the class. Also, go over rules. The following are examples of rules:

1. Don't make fun of others.

2. If you fall on purpose, you will have to sit in chair while rest of class continues.

3. Maintain a quiet voice; no yelling.

Ideas for Motor Breaks

Take a fast walk, such as a quick walk down the hallway or around the room

Walk taking giant steps forward and backward

Use frog jumps or other animal walks

Engage in parachute activities

Try a relay race with erasers

Perform jumping jacks

Try yoga, making sure to choose poses that are easily adapted for children with poor balance and decreased muscle tone.

Practice crossing the midline—crossing over midline is great for brain stimulation. One example is to take your right elbow and touch your left knee (raise knee to waist height); then repeat with left elbow and right knee.

Perform windmills—touch toes with opposite hand

Volume

Students may yell or talk very loud for a variety of reasons. These students must learn to use their voice appropriately so they will not disturb the entire class and so they are socially accepted.

There are two simple ways to help students use the appropriate volume when talking. The first is to record real conversations the student is having. Play back the recording and have the student identify when his or her voice is too loud or too soft. The other way is to use visual cues. Use colors or pictures attached to a paint stick or wooden spoon for visual cues. You may also place a chart on the students' desk or on the board. As the students' voice becomes loud, you can point to the level the child should be using.

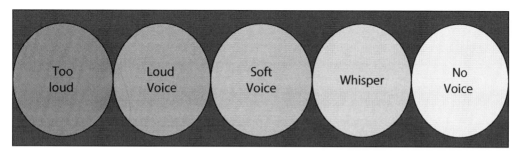

Fidgets

Fidgets allow students to move and still concentrate without disturbing the entire class. Some children need hand or foot fidgets whereas others may need mouth fidgets.

> Some examples of hand fidgets are textured balls squeeze balls and mini hand massagers
>
> Some students are prone to throw items. Balls and small fidgets are not a good choose for these students. A sensory strip may be used instead.
>
> A sensory strip is simply a strip of material or Velcro with multiple textures attached. The strip may be placed under the desk so other students will not see it.
>
> Pencil fidgets and pencil fidget toppers are ideal for even older children.

An exercise band can be tied to the leg of desk chairs to provide resistive movement for legs. But fidgets are not ideal for everyone. Students who have difficulty terminating (stopping) an activity or students who have difficulty with transition may not benefit from fidgets.

Oral Motor Activities and Tools

Have parents incorporate chewy and crunchy foods into the student's diet such as bagels or granola for breakfast. Try beef jerky, dry cereal, or fruit roll-ups for snacks.

Chewy tubes or Chew Stixx pencil toppers.

Positioning

Allow the student to stand to complete work sheets. Tape the worksheet to the wall and outline boundaries using tape or a throw rug.

Use an exercise ball for a chair. Make sure the student's feet touch the floor.

Allow the student to sit on the floor to read.

Attention, Sensory and Behavior

*If you raise your children to feel that they can accomplish any goal
or task they decide upon, you will have succeeded as a parent and
you will have given your children the greatest blessing of all.*
—Brian Tracey

9

Attention, Sensory and Behavior

Children with the diagnosis discussed in this book are often labeled as "behavior problems." Behaviors are simply how a person acts, good or bad. What is most important is to look at is why the student is exhibiting behaviors, good and bad. It is easy to focus on the "bad behaviors," but you must also have a good understanding of why the child is exhibiting "good" behaviors. This will assist you in helping the student maintain the appropriate behaviors. You may have to become an investigator to find the root of the behavior.

Behaviors occur for one of two reasons: Children are seeking or are avoiding. Children often demonstrate inappropriate behaviors when they want something and cannot get it. They may not be allowed to have the wanted item at the time, they may not know how to ask for the item, or they may have to complete a task before obtaining the wanted item or activity. Students may also exhibit seeking behaviors in an attempt to obtain attention from an adult or classmates. Unwanted behaviors may also occur when the student is attempting to avoid a task. The task may be too difficult; it may provide unwanted sensory input, or the student may be afraid of the potential sensory input.

It is important to record data regarding the student's behavior, again, both good and bad. A sensory concern may easily be identified by looking at when the student does not exhibit unwanted behaviors. For example, a student may consistently have unwanted behaviors in science class but never in math class. The math classroom is set up with individual desk facing the board. Assignments are always written in the right corner of the board. The walls are beige and free of posters. The science room is set with six students to a table. There are a variety of posters around the green classroom. There are many items scattered around the room and assignments are only given verbally.

The student presents with over-responsiveness to tactile and visual stimuli and prefers structure: Sitting close to peers at the table is frightening. The posters and other items around the room are overwhelming. Verbal directions are difficult to follow resulting in stress and anxiety. Having the ability to compare settings and "good" and "bad" behaviors provide you with a possible explanation for the outburst.

There are specific questions to ask when analyzing the students' behavior"

- When and where do the unwanted behaviors occur?
- What are the surroundings when the behaviors occur?
  - Are odors different in the setting?
  - Are sounds different in the setting?

- Does the student understand what is expected of him or her?
- Are the physical requirements of the task too difficult or too easy
- Does the task have meaning?
- Does the student need individual attention?
- How are you approaching the student?

The first four questions are related. It is important to identify if behaviors occur in different settings (classroom, lunchroom, gym, and hall). What is it about the setting that may be overstimulating?

Does the student understand what is expected of him or her?

Often it is assumed that students understand directions, assignments, and expected behaviors. However, many students need very clear verbal and written expectations. They may also need frequent reminders. Expectations must be clearly defined and should not vary from day to day.

Students who are unsure of what is expected may be anxious and fearful resulting in flight or fright responses. Expectations that change daily are confusing, resulting in frustration and acting out. Daily report cards and written and/or picture schedules are simple solutions to these behaviors.

Are the physical requirements of the task too difficult or too easy?

Students with sensory motor deficits or poor coordination may have difficulty with what is seen as a simple task. Students may have difficulty gathering the correct books and notebooks or even putting items into their backpack. Cutting with scissors, writing, and even lining numbers up for simple math problems may be too difficult for some children. Can the task be broken down into smaller steps? Are there organization techniques that can be used to assist the student? Can items be eliminated for the student? Can the child type his or her assignments? Could graph paper be used to assist with math?

If the task is too easy or is unable to keep the student's attention, can you add a challenge? Could the student stand on a balance disc while completing their math worksheet? Can the student assist peers? If the student consistently finishes activities first, have worksheets for the student to complete or "chores" for the student.

Does the task have meaning?

Many students have fixations on specific objects, such as cars or dinosaurs. If the activity does not involve their interest, they will not participate. There are times you can incorporate the students' interest. You can have young students count animals or cars or identify the colors. You can have the student write sentences about their interest or even read books. However, there are times when this is not an option. Positive reinforcement can be used in these situations. For example, the student must complete their math worksheets before they are allowed to read a portion of their book about cars. A time limit must be established when using this technique. The student would be allowed to read a portion of a book for a specific number of minutes.

A timer can be set, and when the designated period ends, the student would transition to the next scheduled task.

Does the student need individual attention?

Some students may interrupt, stand at the teacher's desk, or ask for assistance more than needed. These behaviors certainly can be a result of impulsiveness. They may also be attention seeking. A student may be seeking personal attention from the teacher for a variety of reasons. Their attempts to gain attention may be disruptive to the entire class. Are there a few minutes each day that can be set aside for the student? If this is an option, be very clear regarding the time of day and the amount of time. Students who need more than a few minutes daily should be referred to the school councilor.

How are you approaching the student?

Approach does make a difference. Some children do not respond to demands, or their response may not be positive. Yes, students need to be able to follow directions and rules. Being aware of our words and approach can help, not hinder, this expectation.

Allow the student to have some control. Are you using the phrase "I said to?" Try asking, "What did I ask you to do?" If the student is using a daily schedule, you can ask, "What should you be doing right now?" This allows the student to think through the situation and prevents a power struggle.

Power struggles often occur when a student insists on doing what he or she wants to do and refuses all other tasks. Allow the child to choose an activity, and set a time limit. Then you choose the next task. Again, a time limit is set. The student is able to understand the task you choose will end at a designated time and that he or she will be allowed to choose once again. A visual timer and picture choices are beneficial when using this approach.

Picture choices allow choices within limits that you set. You have two or three pictures of task that the student enjoys and are acceptable. You also have two or three picture choices that you need the student to complete. The student is allowed to choose only from the pictures you present. Then the student is shown the picture of what is expected next (your choice). The picture is placed on his or her schedule board. Set the visual timer, allowing the student to complete the task he or she chose. Then the student is presented with the task you have selected from his or her schedule board. Remind the student that he or she will get to choose next but that "this task" must be completed. Set the timer.

Common behaviors have been discussed. Flow charts to assist in problem solving follows.

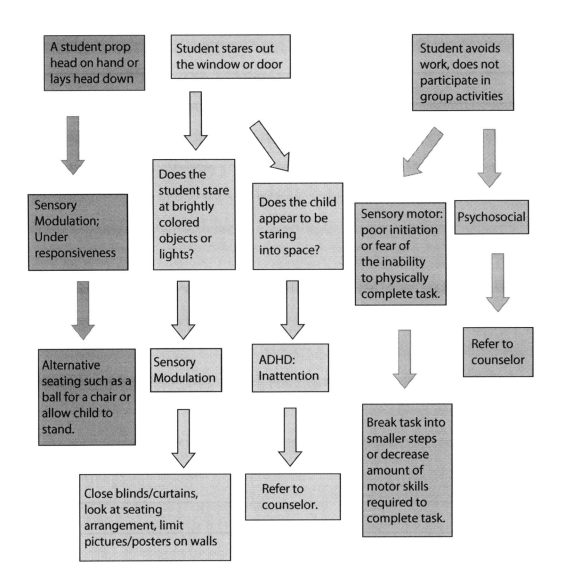

Student refuses to participate in activity

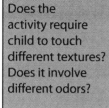

Does the activity require child to touch different textures? Does it involve different odors?

Does the activity involve multiple steps? Does the activity involve Skills that may be difficult for child?

Was this activity scheduled?

Children who are very structured have difficulty with unexpected activities.

Sensory Modulation: Over-resposnsiveness

Sensory motor

Modify the activity. If the child has to glue, use stick glue. If markers are needed use colored pencils or crayons to avoid the smell.

Can the task be broken down into smaller task? Can part of the activity be "pre-assembled"? Can you provide written or visual directions?

Schedule task and provide verbal cues throughout the day reminding them of the task.

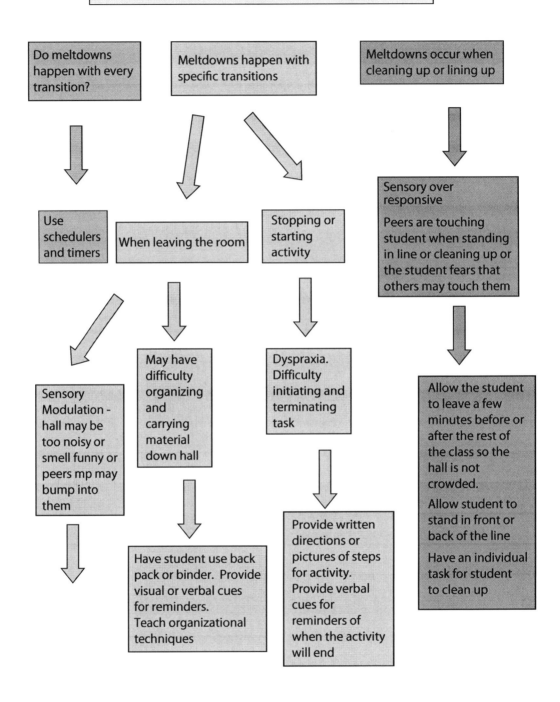

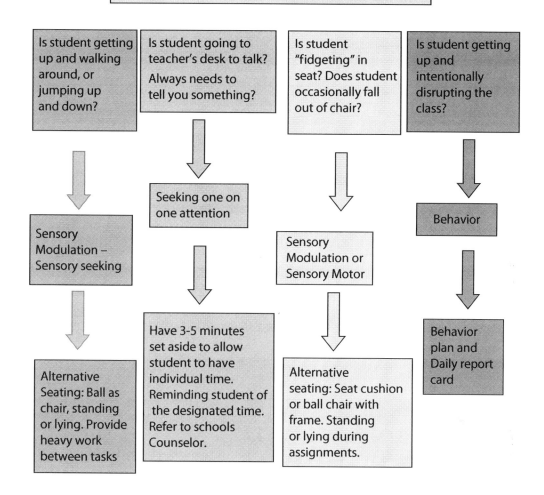

Student will not remain seated or sit still

Is student getting up and walking around, or jumping up and down?

Is student going to teacher's desk to talk?

Always needs to tell you something?

Is student "fidgeting" in seat? Does student occasionally fall out of chair?

Is student getting up and intentionally disrupting the class?

Seeking one on one attention

Sensory Modulation – Sensory seeking

Sensory Modulation or Sensory Motor

Behavior

Alternative Seating: Ball as chair, standing or lying. Provide heavy work between tasks

Have 3-5 minutes set aside to allow student to have individual time. Reminding student of the designated time. Refer to schools Counselor.

Alternative seating: Seat cushion or ball chair with frame. Standing or lying during assignments.

Behavior plan and Daily report card

Student has frequent outburst

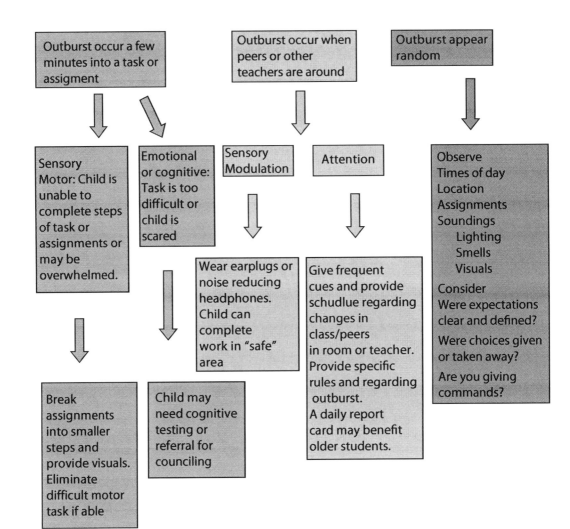

Outburst occur a few minutes into a task or assigment

Outburst occur when peers or other teachers are around

Outburst appear random

Sensory Motor: Child is unable to complete steps of task or assignments or may be overwhelmed.

Emotional or cognitive: Task is too difficult or child is scared

Sensory Modulation

Attention

Observe
Times of day
Location
Assignments
Soundings
   Lighting
   Smells
   Visuals

Consider
Were expectations clear and defined?

Were choices given or taken away?

Are you giving commands?

Wear earplugs or noise reducing headphones. Child can complete work in "safe" area

Give frequent cues and provide schudlue regarding changes in class/peers in room or teacher. Provide specific rules and regarding outburst. A daily report card may benefit older students.

Break assignments into smaller steps and provide visuals. Eliminate difficult motor task if able

Child may need cognitive testing or referral for counciling

Many children have a difficult time identifying and expressing their emotions appropriately. Students may physically act out because they do not know how to control their feelings. Often emotions have to be taught, as does the appropriate way to handle these emotions. Emotion cards are a great way to do this.

To make emotion cards begin by choosing the type of picture to use. You may choose smiley faces, pictures of children, and/or stick people.

Make a picture card with happy, sad, mad and frustrated and appropriate responses for each emotion. The teacher will then identify the emotions and appropriate responses for each emotion. For example, if the student is frustrated, he or she can ask for help. If angry, he or she can squeeze play dough or a pillow. If choices are provided to do these or similar actions, the materials must be readily available. If you offer choices that are not available, it will most likely result in acting out.

EMOTION	Word	What Can You Do?
	Happy	Clap Smile
	Sad	Ask for a hug.
	Mad	Go to calm area. Choose item from angry box.
	Frustrated	Ask for help.

Now you must teach the student how to identify these emotions. When the student displays these emotions, point to the picture, say the emotion and read the choices available to properly demonstrate the emotion. The emotion card may be placed on the student's desk. If you are using this technique for the entire class, post it on the wall as a reminder for all students.

For children who may get angry easily develop an angry box. This box should have multiple choices to help the student calm. Having play dough, clothespins, a ball to squeeze, and a toy that can be pulled and stretched are good starters.

Anger

Everyone becomes angry, including children. It is important to acknowledge these feelings. Ignoring it or expecting students to get over it results in more outburst and inappropriate reactions. Teach students it is OK to be angry and teach them what is and is not appropriate reactions.

Anger Rules	
It's OK to be angry.	
But it is not OK	
to hurt others or	
to tear up toys.	

The "Safe Place"

This is an area set up to allow students to calm down. Students may need this area if they are overstimulated, upset, or angry. The area should provide privacy and items to assist the student in calming. The space is to be used for short periods. The use of the area should be clearly explained to students. The student should be aware that their work must still be completed. They may choose to bring their work to the safe area, they may choose to finish it as homework, or you may establish another option. The safe area is to provide a space that is safe and calm, not an area to avoid work.

Case Studies

*What all good teachers have in common, however, is
that they set high standards for their students
and do not settle for anything less.*
                                        —Marva Collins

10

Case Studies

Case Study: Crisden
    Age: 6 years 6 months
    Classroom: Typical first-grade classroom

Signs/Symptoms

Always touching

Stays seated in chair 2 minutes

Stays seated on floor 4–5 minutes

Moves around room continuously

Teacher concerns

Does not stay seated

When up, touches other students

Appears uninterested in academics

When in small groups, looks around, reaches across table to touch others

In large group, stares off, props on hands, slides out of chair

When sitting on rug, will lie down or scoot around

Solution	Reason	How to Implement
Crisden's desk should be in the middle of room in the first or second row, an arm's length from others	Unable to touch others and is in teacher's line of vision	
On cushion in chair during large group	Allows slight movement in desk chair	Use thick cushion or therapy cushion, ensuring feet touch the floor
Ball seat during small group	Increased attention	Use yoga or therapy ball ensuring feet touch floor
Visual boundaries during floor time	Visuals will increase awareness of personal space	Tape boundaries or use carpet square
Visual boundaries for small group	Visuals will increase awareness of personal space	Use chalk or tape to draw boundaries on the table

(Continued)

Solution	Reason	How to Implement
Standing to complete worksheets	Allows movement and creates interest	Tape worksheet to chalkboard or to another designated area.
When walking around classroom firmly touch students shoulder	Firm pressure will provide sensory input as well as tactile cues to refocus.	Use whole hand, place on shoulder and press firmly, briefly.
Allow student to place chair on tables and wipe board	Provides "heavy work" activities and movement	
Do not take away PE	Student needs movement, taking away opportunities to move will result in higher need to move	If the student has been in trouble and you do not feel it is fair for him to do something fun still allow PE but no group activity. Running, throwing ball against wall and catching it, or cleaning up the gym are good alternatives.

Case Study: Doug

> **Age:** 8 years old
> **Classroom**
>
> Typical third-grade classroom
> Student has IEP
> Receives speech therapy twice a week

Diagnosis: Autism Spectrum Disorder (Asperger)

> **Signs/Symptoms**
>
> Transitions are difficult
> Tantrums
> Stereotypical behaviors including hand flapping and toe walking
> Very literal
> Does not like to be touched
> Avoids touching soft, sticky, and rough items

Teacher concerns

> Changing subjects requires coaxing.
> Changing classes often takes more than 10 minutes, and at least once every two weeks, he will not go.
> When in line, he becomes very upset often screaming if another student gets too close.
> If items he does not like are placed on his lunch tray, he will yell, refuse to eat, or drop his tray purposefully.

Refuses to participate in activities that require glue or paint

Defiant. Will tell teacher no or say, "I don't want too"

Solutions	Reasons	How to Implement
Visual schedule	He will be able to see what comes next.	Using pictures make a schedule. Be sure to include all aspects of the day.
Visual timer	He will be able to see that the activity will end.	Visual schedule can be downloaded on iPad or purchased
Have him be line leader or at the end of the line	He will be able to stand away from peers but still be in line.	
Be clear and use the same language	He is literal. Changing wording or joking does not make sense to him.	
Do not ask if there is really no option. Limit choices and do not ask open ended questions	He is literal.	Do not ask, "Are you ready to go" if it is time to go. Do not ask, "What do you want to do?" Ask would you like to do A or B.
Personal story	For lunchtime	Develop a social story that addresses items on his lunch tray.
Use glue sticks and paint brushes	Participation is more important than the items used to reach the goal	Demonstrate how using the glue stick will not get glue on his hands. Demonstrate how to gently dip paintbrush on paint, reassuring him that if it does get on him that he can wipe his hands. Have hand wipes within reach.
Implement consequences	Consequences must be clear and enforced consistently	IEP team must complete behavior plan. Sit down with the student and explain rules and consequences. If necessary, provide a copy of rules and consequences so that he can see them daily.
Provide object to take during transition.	Providing reminders prior to transactions will prepare him. Having an object to bring to the next room will give him purpose.	Provide visual timer. Provide verbal reminders at 5, 3, 2, and 1 minute that transition is going to happen. Provide an object to take to the next room and have a location he must place the item. A small book may be a good choice or PECS.
Integrated Listening System	Decrease anxiety and assist with focus and transition	3 times per week during tabletop activities

Case Study: Clarisa

Age: 8 years old
Classroom

Typical second-grade classroom
No special services at school

Receives outpatient occupational therapy twice a week

Sees counselor for anxiety

Recently moved to new school

Has very supportive family

Problems making and keeping new friends

Diagnosis: anxiety, lack of coordination

Signs/Symptoms

Transitions are difficult

Tantrums

Cries easily

Low self-esteem

Poor fine motor skills

Difficulty sleeping at night

Teacher concerns

Cries when not performing well

Poor handwriting—reversals

Cannot tie shoes

Difficulty making friends

Does not like excessive noise

Solutions	Reasons	How to Implement
Oral spelling test along with written test	Reversals are not counted against her performance.	Take average of both tests. Give test in small group to prevent anxiety.
Visual timer	She will be able to see that the activity will end.	Set timer where she is able to see the time left before next activity/lesson
Oral and written directions	Prevent meltdowns when she forgets what she heard	She will be able to read directions if she forgets what she heard.
Be clear and use the same language	She gets feelings hurt easily.	Speak to class as a whole and then ask her if she understood what was said (ask privately)
Allow her and others to sit on therapy ball chair	Proprioceptive input to hips for calming/organizing	Allow students to use therapy ball chairs in room.
Rest breaks	To give time to regroup self and have a mental break	Have class as a whole do stretching especially prior to test.

Gross motor movement in PE	Allows for proprioceptive movement	Crossing midline activities such as Brain Gym
Extra time for written work	To decrease stress for her	Set up with her and her parents that she is able to take home the work not finished in class or will be graded on what is finished
Variety of pencil grippers, use variety of pencil leads such as #4 lead	Poor handwriting	Have a variety of pencil grippers (ask OT) and thickness of pencil leads such as a #3, or #4 lead
E-mail or contact parent/caregiver	So teacher will have knowledge if student had a bad night of sleep or change in household	Set up a communication folder or e-mail system so daily communication is available

Case Study: Ella

    Age: 5 years old

    Classroom

        Typical prekindergarten classroom

        No special services at school

        Receives outpatient occupational therapy twice a week

        Wore bilateral foot orthotics

        Recently moved to new school

        Very supportive family

Diagnosis: Lack of coordination, viral infection possible encephalitis at 14 months of age

Signs/Symptoms

        Poor fine motor skills

        Poor gross motor skills—running

        Toileting accidents at school and therapy

        Poor balance

        Covers ears during loud noises, toilet flushing included

        Does not listen to directions

        Messy eater

Teacher concerns

        Does not like excess noise

        Easily disoriented during excessive commotion in room

        Does not know if face is dirty

Toileting accidents at school

Does not follow directions

Solutions	Reasons	How to implement
Timer for toilet time	Get on routine schedule for toileting	Set timer for every 2.5 hours for toilet schedule, toilet prior to leaving room for long periods
Give her 2 buddies in classroom	If one student is absent, she has a second person to be with during fire drills or emergency transitions.	Rotate who is her partner but keep to 2 peers so that decreases confusion, practice emergency drills
Teach her to check face in mirror in bathroom	She is unable to recognize when things are out of order or messy.	After eating she needs to go to bathroom and toilet, followed by looking in mirror.
Be clear and use the same language	Simple directions for her age is easier to follow	Talk directly to her and remind her that she is expected to follow directions. Have her repeat the directions.
Breaks during the day	If she appears to be disorganized she needs a break to restart her processing.	Give her heavy work: carry items, push carts across room or down hall way, run in hallway with paraprofessional for release of energy.
Movement in PE	Gross motor input is calming/organizing to her.	Structured gross motor skills—running, jumping, climbing, rolling during PE
Integrated Listening System	Calming/organizing	Outpatient Occupational Therapy with a home program 5 times per week

Case Study: Ben
    Age: 10 years old
    Classroom

    Typical fourth-grade classroom

    No special services at school

    On medication for ADHD

Diagnosis: ADHD

Signs/Symptoms

    Impulsive

    Inattentive

    Poor handwriting

    Rarely turns in homework

Teacher concerns

    Does not stay seated

    Disrupts class

    Very loud

    Constant cues to complete assignments

    Rarely turns in homework

    Difficulty reading handwriting

Solutions	Reasons	How to implement
Alternative seating with visual boundaries	Less time spent redirecting him to sit. Alternative sitting may also assist with handwriting	Tape off area where student is allowed to stand or sit to complete assignments
Use a timer for assignments	Maintain attention without constant cues	Timer is set and student must work until alarm sounds.
Daily Report Card	Student has clear expectations.	Clearly explain to student and parents the purpose and goal of the daily report card.
Written reminders for books and homework	Teach organizational skills and assist student in returning homework	Student must attempt to write homework down and is responsible for asking teacher to help ensure it is correct. A written list to help student sequence what to bring home can be placed in a specific location.
Teach voice use	Decrease classroom disruptions and improve social skills	Record his voice or use visual reminders.

Letters from Parents to Teachers

There is a brilliant child locked inside every student.
—Marva Collins

11

Letters from Parents to Teachers

Your job is described in one simple word, *teach*. It almost makes your job sound easy. But teaching 18 or more children who have various needs is challenging. The pressure of keeping test scores up and meeting yearly benchmarks can easily take the focus off each individual child. So when children begin to struggle, when an outburst occurs, when homework is not turned in, when they are too tired to hold their eyes open, it is easy to not see the whole picture.

You wonder why the child cannot bring his or her homework back and when he or she does it is not complete. You wonder why the parents will not get their child in bed at a decent hour. You know that if the parents would do these things the child would be more successful.

As teachers, you do not see the struggle it is to get the child dressed. You do not see the tantrum thrown over which shirt to wear. You do not see the gagging as the child's teeth are being brushed. You do not hear the screaming of siblings when one bumps into the other. You do not see the parents exhausted and trying to work on hours of homework while cooking for the family. You do not see the nighttime routine and the attempts to help the child get to sleep before midnight and be up at six.

Three letters from parents to teachers follow. They have been included as a reminder that parents do want the best for their child. And just like your job to teach seems simple, their job to parent is more than a single word.

Dear Mrs. Smith,

I wanted to give you a little background on my daughter, Clara who will be in your class this year. Clara is a wonderful, smart, caring child who has a few "issues". She has developmental delays, sensory processing disorder, and auditory processing disorder, mild hearing loss in one ear, esophoria (eye processing like disorder), asthma and anxiety. Yes, it is a long list, but all items are easily managed. I will address each issue one by one.

Developmental delays:

Clara is currently up to a two-year delay in certain areas. The areas she is most behind in are fine motor and gross motor. Most of the time you will not even notice these as issues, because Clara does not say anything and is quiet in class. We are working with a great OT and have come a long way in a short time. We will continue to address the areas.

Sensory Processing Disorder:

Again, much of this will not be noticed inside the typical classroom setting. For Clara certain textures—mainly on clothing bother her. She does often get "overloaded" with sensory input. If a room has too much loud noise, bright light or even funny smells, Clara can get very agitated. Chewing gum is a very helpful in keeping Clara "grounded" and focused. I will send gum to school and she can have some at anytime. She is really good about asking for gum when needed. If, you notice her chewing her hair, or the end of her pencils please offer her some gum.

Auditory Processing Disorder:

Clara cannot hear certain sounds. This makes reading, spelling, and other schoolwork very challenging. She always does her best, but does not often ask for help because she is shy. When things are being read aloud in class, she may not hear the difference between two words that are similar sounding. This causes compression problems and difficulty taking oral tests (in large settings). You will notice this is an issue in school. Clara does best being near to the teacher and, if able, to be pulled for tests that are given orally, to reduce extra noises and other disruptions. We will work together to make the best plan for what Clara needs inside the class.

Also, loud noises—such as the fire alarm—are very scary to her. Any automatic toilets, hand dryers, or such are horrifying to her. You will notice she will cover her ears a lot. In the past we have used hats or earmuffs to help damping the noises. Lots of noises are scary to her—noises that you or I might not hear, she can hear and often fixates on and is thus unable to accomplish basic tasks. Please let me know if you need me to bring her hat or headphones to school.

Hearing Loss:

Due to a large number of ear infections, Clara has hearing loss in her right ear. So, she needs to be placed in the front of the room, facing the teacher. Again, this is mild and you may not notice it.

Esophoria:

It is best explained as follows: Another eye coordination problem is termed esophoria, which is a tendency for the eyes to turn inwards. The educational implication of this particular problem is that a child with esophoria sees things smaller than what they actually are. In order to see an object properly, it is necessary to make the object larger. The only means at the disposal of the child to make it larger is to bring it closer. Eventually, the child is observed with her head buried in a book and still not achieving.

Clara wears glasses to help with this; they are special type of progressive bifocal type of lenses. She needs to wear them during school. She does not need them at lunch, recess, or PE. I will send her a case she can keep at school.

You will notice that she often squints (if not wearing her glasses) and that she has trouble with basic copying from the board onto her paper or gets overwhelmed at a worksheet of math problems. To help her with this, you can cover up some of the words/problems on the page, so that only a few are seen at the same time. Again, Clara may not say much, and you might only notice when she turns something in and it is different than what was on the board. I can provide you with more ideas and information to help, if needed.

Asthma:

Clara is really good about knowing when she needs to go to the nurse to get her inhaler or treatment. The big thing to know is she cannot be outside if the grass is being mowed. This will set off an asthma attack. Again, Clara is really good about letting people know she should not be outside when grass is being mowed.

Anxiety:

This is a big one. Clara takes medication everyday to help and sees a therapist on a weekly basis. Her therapist will come to the school and see her during the school day. Clara is pretty good about asking for a "time-out" to cool off and collect herself. It is important for Clara and you to have a "code" word that she can use if she needs to leave the room. For time-outs at school, she can go to the counselor, the office, or just sit in the hallway—whatever is best. Changes in routine are challenging and often evoke anxiety in Clara. Making sure any schedule changes are known, is a big help. She has been know to cry, to scream, or to try to run away from a teacher when she has reached a breaking point. Just stay calm, speak softly, and give her some space. The school counselor knows about Clara's issues and can help at anytime during the school day.

Social Concerns:

Over all Clara is a smart, fun, kind child. School is challenging for her due to all her issues. One thing to be on the lookout for is the Clara is often bullied. This has happened several times—sometimes she does not know she is getting picked on; she thinks her "friends" are just playing with her, when they are really being mean and hurtful. Clara is a loner and only has a few friends. She likes to swing and play on the merry-go-round at recess. I will let you know if she mentions anything to me about being bullied, so we can work together to get this taken care of quickly.

I just wanted to provide you with some basic information about Clara. I know we will have several official meeting at school to go over her Section 504 plans and address any and all accommodations she needs at school. Most of the time Clara is fun, quiet, and very helpful. I am here is you need anything or have any questions.

Thanks for your support and I look forward to a great school year!

Thanks
Clara's mom

Dear Ms. Jones,

I wanted to give you a little background on my daughter, Stella, who will be in your class this year. Stella is a wonderful, smart, and funny little child who has a few "issues." She has a sensory processing disorder, hypertonia (poor muscle tone), and encephalopathy (illness of the brain). She currently gets OT and PT for a total of 4 times a week. I have spoken to Ms. Johnson at the school and started the PPCD paperwork. I wanted to give you some more information on Stella.

How to tell is Stella is having a sensory overload:

She gets really quiet
She says, "Too loud" or "Too bright"
She avoids eye contact
She starts to make sounds instead of talking
She starts flapping her arms
She starts making something else make noise—repeatedly
She starts sucking on something
She starts rocking
She asks to be wrapped up

What to do when she is having a sensory "meltdown":

Try to calm her.
Get her out of the situation/area—if known.
Talk in a calm and quiet voice.
Ask what she wants—she make not answer, but she may nod or point to what she wants.
Make sure she does not hurt herself or other—she is known to start throwing things (repeatedly) when melting down.
Just be there for her—sometimes it just has to run its course and there is nothing you can do to help her.
Most of the times a "meltdown" lasts only about 10 minutes, but it can last up to an hour.

Triggers:

Being tired
Being hungry
Loud noises
Bright lights
Grass
Uneven surfaces, like walking on sand

Things that can calm her down:

Rocking
Sucking
Playing with her hands, like in water or shaving cream
Swaddling in a blanket
Headphones or a hat with ear flaps
A quiet and darker corner

What can Stella do:

She can do anything she wants, but still needs help with certain things. These things include going up or down stairs; carrying things (lunch tray); climbing into a tall chair; holding a pencil, scissors, etc.; getting her shoes on or off; squeezing things like a glue bottle.

Other notes:

Stella cannot tell the difference between hot and cold, so she may overheat in the warmer months and think she does not need a jacket in the colder months. Also, she is very messy. She is just starting to say she needs to wash her hands or face if they are messy. She may need reminders to wash her hands.

I just wanted to give you information to help you in the classroom with Stella—most of the time she is happy, funny, and helpful. I am here if you need anything or have any questions.

Thanks
Emily

Amanda,

We are very excited that you are Sam's 4th-grade teacher. As we are also involved in public education—Jeff as a school resource officer and I am a teacher—we know that it literally "takes a village to raise a child" and we both feel that the teacher-parent relationship is a vital component of the "village." So, because we are now a team and, therefore should be 'on the same page,' please indulge me as I share with you information about Sam that we believe it is important for you to know.

Jeff and I adopted Sam when he was just under one year old. He was cocaine positive at birth. Although Sam did not exhibit any manifestations indicating addiction, only exposure, we were informed that, should any manifestations of prenatal drug use present, it would likely be in the form of ADHD appearing at school age, when children are generally first exposed to the daily rigors of school structure.

Indeed, as Sam entered preschool, we did begin to recognize signs of ADHD, specifically great difficulty with sustaining attention and focus during academic activities as well as impulse control. We began several interventions at home in an attempt to combat these symptoms. These interventions included a structured routine with pictorial clues and diet modifications. Minimal to no improvement was noted.

When Sam entered kindergarten at the age of 6, we immediately saw an increase in ADHD characteristics. In fact, the first six weeks of school were, simply stated, a nightmare. Sam had increased difficulty with sustained attention and focus as well as impulse control. His teacher gave only one verbal warning before "moving clips" on the behavior chart. Sam's color-coded behavior chart was a virtual rainbow—just in the first week! Worse, his self-esteem suffered. Daily, I spent up to two hours trying to convince Sam that he was not "bad," as he had been told in school, but that the choices he made were not good ones. We contacted the school counselor, who gave us (and his teacher) a Connors ADHD Rating Scale to complete. Once the counselor compiled these results, we took them to our physician. As I am also a registered nurse, I am very well aware of the perceived and actual abuse of ADHD medications, particularly in school-age children. However, I also firmly believe that these medications do have a legitimate place. Therefore, after much discussion and prayer, we agreed to begin Sam on a small dose of prescription ADHD medication. As our physician put it, "if Sam had diabetes, you wouldn't hesitate to give him medications to help him. Sam has a condition that he, nor we, asked for. But, there are medications available that can help, so why not use them?" Well, the difference in Sam's behavior after beginning the medication was "night and day" and immediate. In fact, the week after beginning the medication, his teacher asked us for permission to have him screened for the G/T program. The remainder of his kindergarten year was, for the most part, uneventful.

Sam's first-grade year was, thus far, his best year ever. His teacher—a wonderful, patient, calming lady—was also the "inclusion" teacher for the grade level. Therefore, she had in-class assistance for several parts of the day. Although Sam was not an inclusion student, he certainly did benefit from the extra attention and assistance. The year passed smoothly and Sam even earned a medal for "All A's Honor Roll" all year! We couldn't help but wonder, though, if the smooth year was attributable to the benefit of the in-class support.

Sam's second-grade year was a close second to his nightmarish kindergarten start. He had two teachers—one for language arts and one for math, science, and social studies. His language arts teacher had a mild-mannered personality, and Sam responded well to her. The partner teacher, however, was quite the opposite. We encountered several issues during the year and began to wonder if we needed to pursue a 504 status for Sam for modifications that would give Sam some help with his academic struggles. For example, one issue was over Sam using his fingers to count with during math. His teacher absolutely forbade it while we encouraged it, knowing that children will generally stop using them once they are comfortable with the concept. He struggled specifically with math facts and reading fluency. In fact, his beginning-of-year Texas Primary Reading Initiative (TPRI) indicated he was reading on a "Frustration" level. As a result, he was referred for evaluation by the Intervention team. He did not qualify for Reading Intervention, but was described as a "messy" reader, though what that means was never explained to me. One of the habits I noted when reading with him was that he substituted words but never changed the meaning of the word/phrase/sentence. For example, if a sentence said "I like to visit my grandmother," Sam might read it as "I like to visit my grandma." In December of this year, I was visiting with a friend—also a teacher—to "compare notes" about what to expect for the second- and third-grade years. As I explained what Sam's year had been like and some of the difficulties we had begun to notice, she, a certified dyslexia teacher, indicated that Sam may be exhibiting markers of dyslexia and recommended evaluation by the Luke Waites Center for Dyslexia and Learning Disorders at Scottish Rite Hospital for Children in Dallas. Not really knowing a lot about dyslexia but wondering about the possibility and wanting to do all we can for our son, we decided to pursue this evaluation. Thus, we began the six-month-long paper trail. Behaviorally, Sam again began to have difficulty with sustained mental focus and attention. So, we again consulted with our physician. Because Sam had gone through a little growth spurt, our physician felt that a slight boost in his medication dose was warranted. Thus, he went from Adderall XR 10mg to Adderall XR 15 mg daily. As we discussed our observations and concerns with our physician and informed him of our plans for evaluation at Scottish Rite, he agreed but suggested that, because of the long wait-time for evaluation at Scottish Rite, we consider evaluation by a local pediatric occupational therapist who would be able to perform some of the same diagnostics. We did, in fact, make an appointment with the OT, who performed a battery of assessments. We discovered that Sam had, in addition to ADHD-Combined Type, a visual processing disorder, and an auditory disorder. Specifically, Sam's eyes didn't track print at the same rate, causing him to reread words numerous times in order to recognize them. Though he has no hearing loss, his ears recognized frequencies at different decibel levels. Following this evaluation, Sam began receiving OT weekly for these findings. During the summer, Sam also attended Auditory Integration Training. In January, we also did request a 504 meeting in order to have some modifications added to help Sam deal with these new findings. This meeting was held at the end of May, and neither Jeff nor I were able to attend. The only modification granted by the committee was "Extended Time." At the conclusion of the school year, we did attend Scottish Rite for evaluation. Sam was not determined to have dyslexia but a concern with motor skills (specifically handwriting) was noted. Thus, OT interventions for this finding were added.

For his third-grade year, Sam began attending a new school. We requested a 504 meeting following the first six weeks. Sam's OT attended with me, and several modifications were added including the use of handwriting paper, preferential seating away from fluorescent lighting, use of a slant board (as Sam had difficulty copying from the vertical SmartBoard to the horizontal position of his paper), and oral test administration in a small group setting. We continue to receive notes indicating that Sam rushes through work, makes silly mistakes, resists writing activities, and is fidgety. We have no evidence that the modifications specified in his 504 are in place currently.

Sam verbalizes, often, that he doesn't like school. He is easily frustrated, does not like to redo activities, and resists extended writing activities. He specifically does not like math, nor is this his strongest subject.

He is a sweet kiddo who loves all bugs and creepy crawlies in general, enjoys video games, has an incredible imagination and extensive vocabulary, and participates in Tae Kwon Do. He continues to receive weekly OT. He is an extremely picky eater and, due to his medication, has a decreased appetite during the day. His medication also has a tendency to increase his thirst and, consequently, the frequency of bathroom visits.

Please forgive me for the length of this letter. However, we are very forthcoming and believe that, in order for you to understand Sam and how best to meet his needs, it is imperative for you to know all of these details. We look forward to working with you this year and are confident that it will be a successful year for Sam. Please do not hesitate to contact us at any time should you have any questions or concerns. We are here to support you.

Blessings,
Jeff and Darlene

Common Questions from Teachers

Keep your face to sunshine and you cannot see the shadow.
—Helen Keller

12

Common Questions from Teachers

What is a reasonable amount of time to keep a child on task?
According to the Student Coalition for Action in Literacy Education, a child's attention span for a learning activity is their chronological age plus one. So, an eight-year-old's attention would be nine minutes. That may seem short, but test yourself. Maintain a seated position and stay on task. The task should be a learning activity, not a hobby.

Using timers, integrating a variety of teaching methods, and allowing alternative seating will assist students in maintaining attention to task.

How can "meltdowns" be prevented?
This is a two-step process. First, you must learn to recognize the signs prior to the behavior or recognize factors that influence behaviors.

The second step is to teach the student to identify the signs and factors and ways to help them handle their emotions appropriately.

Can I make a sensory area and incorporate these strategies myself?
Yes and no. Most children will benefit from or at least enjoy sensory strategies. There are, however, some items that you should steer away from unless it is a recommendation from the student's occupational therapist.

Specialized swings can be a safety concern. First, spinning on a swing gives the sensation of flashing lights. If a child has a seizure disorder, flashing lights may trigger a seizure. Second, movement on the swing directly affects the neurological system. If you place or encourage the child to swing and you are providing movement, you are providing what could be viewed as treatment. Last, there is a risk of injury to the student such as falling off the swing or the swing hitting a student.

The Wilbarger Protocol: Deep Pressure Proprioceptive Touch (DPPT) often referred to as "brushing." This technique should *only* be used for specific children as directed by a trained occupational therapist.

How can sensory strategies be implemented without singling out a student?
Most of the strategies mentioned can be used for the class as a whole. Take time to talk to the class and explain the items that are available to them. Most important, explain the rules for each of the items. Students then have the opportunity to use items as needed.

Where is the school occupational therapist?

For the occupational therapist (OT) to evaluate a student they must have an IEP or 504 and be unable to meet their educational goals due to deficits in fine motor skills, visual perceptual skills, or another area that OT's may specifically address such as sensory processing. Each school has different "rules" regarding OT referral and the criteria to receive this service.

You may request specific requirements for OT services from the special education department or school board. Keep in mind they may not understand that OT's can address sensory processing concerns. Most likely they are unfamiliar with sensory processing disorder. Take the time to educate them. Also remember, not all OT's specialize in sensory processing disorder.

13

Resource Guide

CATALOGS AND GENERAL RESOURCES

Ablenet
800-322-0956

http://www.ablenetinc.com

A great resource for communication aids for nonverbal individuals; access aids for all ages and
situations; and special education classroom curriculum that both enhance and help ensure
learning progress.

Fun and Function
800-231-6329

http://funandfunction.com/

Designs special needs toys, autism toys, and therapy products ideal for occupational therapy
activities for children

Pocket full of Therapy
732-462-4474

http://www.pfot.com/

Sells weighted blankets, desk buddy, organizational pouches for school chairs, and so on

Therapy Shoppe
800-261-5590

http://www.therapyshoppe.com/

Sells large variety of products including slant boards, therapy balls, weighted vests, and inflatable
cushions

Different Roads to Learning
800-853-1057

http://www.difflearn.com

Sells items such as PECS cards, visual timers, auditory games, manipulative, puzzles, and so on

CLOTHING

Soft
www.softclothing.net
Soft is the first brand to address the sensory clothing needs of more than 25% of American
children

In Your Pocket Designs
888-388-3224
www.weightedvest.com
Sells weighted vests and patterns for making your own vest

SCHEDULES

Boardmaker by Dynavox Mayer-Johnson
800-588-4548
www.mayer-johnson.com/

SchKidules
203-441-KIDS (5437)
www.schkidules.com/index.html

SELF-REGULATION

Alert Program Published by Therapy Works Inc.
877-897-3478
www.alertprogram.com/index.php
Program developed by two occupational therapist to be a practical approach to support self-
regulation for all ages and all types of challenges, including autism and ADHD

SOUND THERAPY

Integrated Listening Systems
303-741-4544
www.integratedlistening.com/
ILS programs improve emotional regulation while training the brain to process sensory
information

Berard AIT—Auditory Integration Training
www.berardaitwebsite.com
The Berard method of auditory integration training stimulates the auditory system with unique
sounds produced by the Berard AIT device; it is a method of retraining the way the sounds
are processed.

Interactive Metronome

www.interactivemetronome.com

IM's game-like auditory-visual platform engages the patient and provides constant feedback at the millisecond level to promote synchronized timing in the brain.

Video Modeling/Social Skills Videos

Model Me Kids

888-938-3240

www.modelmekids.com/

Demonstrate social skills by modeling peer behavior at school, on a playdate, at a birthday party, on the playground, at a library, at the dentist, at a restaurant, and more. Designed as a teaching tool for children, adolescents, and teenagers with autism, Asperger syndrome, and developmental delays, the videos are used by teachers, parents, and therapists. Real children model each skill.

Social Skill Builders

866-278-1452

www.socialskillbuilder.com/

Social Skill Builder's curriculum of researched-based, evidence-driven software programs use systematic and explicit instruction through interactive videos to teach key social thinking, language, and behavior that are critical to everyday living.

TV Teacher

770-971-0450

www.tvteacher.com

Developed by an occupational therapist who performs video-modeling programs to special-needs classes for handwriting and fine motor skills. This program can be used by all students for assistance with handwriting.

Diagnosis-Specific Information

CDC—The Centers for Disease Control and Prevention

800-CDC-INFO (800-232-4636)

http://www.cdc.gov/Features/adhdresources/

Attention Deficit Hyperactivity Disorder

Attention Deficit Disorder Resources

http://www.addresources.org/node/10

Attention Deficit Disorder Resources maintains an educational website and a bookstore. They publish a monthly eNews, the ADHD Reader, and an outstanding collection of articles for adults and parents by national ADHD authorities as well as adults with ADHD.

Autism

Autism Research Institute

www.autism.com

Dedicated to the research and education on the causes of autism and on methods of preventing, diagnosing, and treating autism.

Developmental Delay Resources

www.devdelay.org

DDR is dedicated to meeting the needs of children with developmental delays in sensory, motor, language, social, and emotional areas.

Autism Society of America
301-657-0881

www.autism-society.org

Leading source of information on autism

Autism Speaks
888-AUTISM2

www.autismspeaks.org

One of the largest foundations in the world solely dedicated to autism.

References

American Occupational Therapy Association (AOTA). *Occupational Therapy in School Settings.* Bethesda: AOTA, 2010.

American Physical Therapy Association (APTA). *Physical Therapy in School Settings.* Accessed at www.apta.org/uploadedFiles/APTAorg/Advocacy/Federal/Legislative_Issues/IDEA_ESEA/PhysicalTherapyintheSchoolSystem.pdf.

American Psychiatric Association. *Diagnostic and Statistical Manual of Mental Disorders.* 5th edition. Arlington, VA: American Psychiatric Association, 2013. Print.

Ayres, Jean. *Sensory Integration and the Child: 25th Anniversary Edition.* Torrance, CA: Western Psychological Services, April 1, 2005. Print.

Bagatell N., G. Mirigliani, C. Patterson, Y. Reyes, and L. Test. "Effectiveness of therapy ball chairs on classroom participation in children with autism spectrum disorders." *American Journal of Occupational Therapy 64.6* (2010): 895-903.

Benson, Mary T. *Parent Fact Sheet: Signs and Symptoms of Sensory Processing Disorder.* Newton: The Spiral Foundation, 2006. Print.

Blunder, S. L., C. M. Milte, and N. Simm. "Diet and Sleep in Children with Attention Deficit Hyperactivity Disorder: Preliminary Data in Australian Children." *Journal of Child Health Care* 15.1 (2011):14-24.

Breus, Michael J. "Good, Sound Sleep for Your Child: Making Sure Your Child Gets Good, Sound Sleep Ensures He or She Will Have a Sound Foundation for Proper Mind and Body Development." *WebMD Feature.* June 2, 2003, updated Oct. 21, 2004. Web. Accessed at http://children.webmd.com/features/good-sound-sleep-for-children.

Children's Defense Fund. Child Nutrition Fact Sheet. July 2010 . http://www.childrensdefense.org/child-research-data-publications/data/child-nutrition-factsheet.pdf. Web.

Cermack, S. A. "Somatodyspraxia." *Sensory Integration Theory and Practice.* Ed. A. G. Fischer, A. M. Murray, A. C. Bundy. Philadelphia, PA: F. A. Davis Company, 1991. Print.

The Centers for Disease Control and Prevention. *2008 Physical Activity Guidelines for Americans.* Web. N.d. Accessed at www.cdc.gov.

Franzone, E., and Collet-Klingenberg, L. *Overview of video modeling.* Madison, WI: The National Professional Development Center on Autism Spectrum Disorders, Waisman Center, University of Wisconsin. 2008. Print.

Grandin, Temple. *The Way I See It: A Personal Look at Autism & Asperger's.* Arlington, TX: Future Horizons, 2008. Print

Gajre, N. S., S. Fernandez, N. Balakrishna, and S. Vazir. "Breakfast Eating Habit and its Influence on Attention-Concentration, Immediate Memory and School Achievement." *Indian Pediatrics* 45.10 (2008):824-828. Print.

Interdisciplinary Council on Developmental and Learning Disorders. *Diagnostic Manual for Infancy and Early Childhood Mental Health, Developmental, Regulatory-Sensory Processing, Language and Learning Disorders (ICDL-DMIC).* Bethesda, MD: Interdisciplinary Council on Developmental and Learning Disorders. 2005. Print.

Kerby, Amanda. "Effects of Breaks on Elementary School Students' Classroom Behaviors." *St. Mary's College of Maryland. Rising Tide,* 4 (Summer 2011): 1-22

Scharf, Rebecca J., Ryan T. Demmer, Ellen J. Silver, and Ruth E. K. Stein. "Nighttime Sleep Duration and Externalizing Behaviors of Preschool Children". Journal of Developmental & Behavioral Pediatrics. 34.6 (2013): 384-391. Print.

Schilling D. L., K. Washington, F. F. Billingsley, and J. Deitz. "Classroom Seating for Children with Attention Deficit Hyperactivity Disorder: Therapy Balls Versus Chairs." *American Journal of Occupational Therapy* 57.7 (2003): 534-41. Print

The University of North Carolina at Chapel Hill - School of Education. Carrboro, NC.

Volpe, Robert J., and Gregory A. Fabiano. *Daily Behavior Report Cards: An Evidence-Based System of Assessment and Intervention.* Lay-flat edition. New York: Guilford Press, 2013. Print.

Printed in Great Britain
by Amazon